The God of Science

THE GOD
OF SCIENCE

Personal interviews with 38 leading American and European scientists on the nature of truth, the existence of God, and the role of the church

Frederick E. Trinklein

WILLIAM B. EERDMANS PUBLISHING COMPANY
Grand Rapids, Michigan

To my wife,

MARGARET,

for a quarter century
of love,
discernment,
and motivation

"In the beginning, God. . . ."

Contents

Preface

At the turn of the century, Andrew D. White, the first president of Cornell University, wrote a book entitled, *A History of the Warfare of Science and Theology in Christendom*. It is an imposing work, filling two volumes and more than eight hundred pages. The author, a qualified scientist, saw the controversy between science and · the churches as an unequal battle, with outmoded, mystical dogmas on one side and enlightened, progressive scientific achievements on the other.

How true is this picture? If it is indeed a battle, how is it faring today? Do present-day scientists agree with Dr. White's view? Is religious thought gradually being supplanted by the scientific method? Are churches merely the last vestiges of a dying philosophy?

In this book, today's scientists are sounded out on these questions. It is a forum on science and religion for those who are making these questions daily more urgent through their professional activities. Informally, and in the language of the layman, it takes on a topic that grows in importance with each additional space shot and organ transplant.

Are modern men of science still interested in such matters? Listen:

I don't know any individuals among my scientific **Anderson**
friends, the mature ones who have gotten over the
twenty-five-year age where they think of nothing

ix

but science, who haven't in their own minds in some way and from time to time examined the issue of science and religion. They try to reach some sort of a rationale of their own.

Friedrich   *We discuss religion at work. The majority of scientists in our lab are very interested in it. But they are very skeptical. There is a large number of agnostics, but very few atheists.*

Rydberg   *There are scientists who believe in religion. Unfortunately, I have felt sometimes that they feel they are superior. This is a kind of self-righteousness. It makes many of us who don't believe skeptical toward those who do believe.*

Hansen   *I never believed that, in my lifetime, I could see the possibility of the institutionalized church passing out of existence. I do believe that, unless changes are made, this can indeed be the case.*

If there is a battle between scientists and churchmen, what are the issues? Are they avoidable? Do scientists today see a basic conflict between their work and religious belief? How do their personal convictions compare with the tenets of modern religious denominations?

In the following pages, thirty-eight scientists candidly answer these questions. Throughout the book, the statements of these scientists are printed in a contrasting typeface. They can be identified by the last name of the scientist, which appears in bold-face type in the margin, as above. For the complete names and positions of these scientists, see the alphabetical list following the Preface.

How the Study Was Made

Books and articles on religion usually promote the viewpoint of the writer. This is certainly an author's prerogative, but it disqualifies the work as an objective examination of the topic. Even the choice of a topic can be biased toward a pre-conceived verdict.

Similarly, in order to sample the opinion of the scientific community validly on a specific question, the selection of contributing scientists must not be restricted to those with a particular viewpoint. It should rather be a random selection.

In view of this, and in order to make the study as representative as possible, the following guidelines were used in choosing contributors to the book:

1) European as well as American views should be presented.

2) Contributors should represent a variety of scientific fields.

3) Contributors should be in leadership positions, with an emphasis on educational posts.

4) Choices should be as random as possible.

To satisfy the first requirement, the latest edition of *The World of Learning* was used as a primary source of names. This annual work lists the faculties of colleges and universities around the world. Since a large share of scientific leadership rests today in American and European hands, the selections were made from these countries.

In making the choices, and throughout the book, the layman's interpretation of "scientist" is used. It includes engineers, medical men, astronomers, biologists, chemists, geologists, oceanographers, physicists—men whose training and work involve the laboratory method in the study of man and his physical universe and whom laymen and churchmen alike would clearly categorize as professional scientists.

The choice of educational institutions as a principal source of names is a somewhat arbitrary one. Those who work with youth, especially in the capacity of training them for tomorrow's scientific leadership, should be giving considerable thought to the questions that make up this study. If the book is to provide guidelines for the future, educators ought to have some significant contributions to make.

But not all the selections were from the schools. A number of prominent industries and other agencies were also selected.

Professional stature was based primarily on recognition and position. The most widely acclaimed scientific award in the world is the Nobel Prize. Consequently, a representative number of names was chosen from this list. In the schools, deanship is usually considered the top of the academic ladder. A large percentage of names represents this position. Finally, some names were chosen because of widely known achievements or because of the recommendations of fellow scientists.

Within these parameters, the selections were entirely random. In only two cases did the author know the religious leanings of the contributors in advance, and then only in a very general way.

After the selection of names, personal interviews were requested by mail or telephone. To ensure the spontaneity of the discussions, specific questions were not listed in the requests, but only that the interviews would deal with science and religion and that they would be objectively presented in a book.

The response was overwhelming. Over half of those contacted responded affirmatively, many of them enthusiastically so. Of the negative responses, a large number cited the pressure of time and work as the reason for declining the interview. Several were on extended travels.

There were, of course, some more direct refusals. One well-known scientist replied that he "never discusses sex, politics, or religion." A Nobel Prize winner said that he is already in so much trouble over his political views that he cannot afford to add religious squabbles to the list. Several were simply "not interested." One world-famous physicist granted an interview and then decided to withhold his permission to publish it. A number of requests were sent to scientists in Iron Curtain countries, but none of them replied.

Spontaneity and Objectivity

Since the contributors had no advance knowledge of the questions in the interviews, their replies have a ring of spontaneity that is uncommon in books on this topic. It is not a collection of carefully prepared essays. It is rather a series of informal conversations with prominent scientists in their homes or offices—person-to-person interactions with men and their candid thoughts on science and religion. There is the feeling of listening in on an after-dinner conversation, which indeed was sometimes the case.

The pertinent parts of the interviews averaged about an hour in length. In all but two cases they were tape recorded. This made for an ease of expression and flow of ideas not possible while taking notes. If the tape recorder produced any "stage fright," it was only momentary and probably even had the good result of greater attention to syntax.

The chapter headings represent the main topics of the study. Each man had the opportunity to expand on these topics at will. The specific questions cited within the chapters were used, where appropriate, to develop specific thoughts. Obviously, no two interviews covered precisely the same set of questions, but every contributor had the chance to express himself on every major point.

In each interview, the author maintained a strict impartiality on the questions under discussion. In fact, a number of the interviews were granted only after it was made clear that the study was completely unbiased and independent and did not represent the efforts of a specific church body or publisher. At no time was the contributor involved in a verbal debate, except perhaps with himself or with some unspoken ideology. On occasion, the author was asked for his own views, but these were given entirely off the record and usually after the conclusion of the taped interview.

Each contributor was able to read a transcript of his interview prior to publication. In several cases, the transcripts were also English translations by the author. Few changes or deletions were made by the contributors. Most of them dealt with sentence structure or redundancies. Only one man expressed dissatisfaction with his contribution, but he did not withdraw his permission for publication.

Aside from their value in the science-religion dialog, the interviews were richly rewarding personal experiences. Each one of the meetings was most cordial and, almost to a man, the contributors felt that the study was important and they were eager to see the results in printed form.

How to Read This Book

One might argue that the opinions of thirty-eight scientists hardly constitute a meaningful segment of scientific thinking. (Perhaps one could apply a similar argument to the highly touted public opinion polls of our day.) The book does not claim to be a poll. The number of interviews is arbitrarily limited. No special formulas were or should be used to derive special meanings from the frequency or length of specific responses. Some scientists are simply more talkative than others, and this attribute is not necessarily related to their viewpoint on a specific topic.

Man does not live and think by polls alone. Some of the contributors even emphasized this point. We reach conclusions, we make decisions by impressions gained from personal interactions, many of them quite by chance. In this spirit, thirty-eight chance encounters with leading scientists are recounted here for the reader's vicarious benefit. The effect is not meant to be conclusive. Many more contributors, with many more opinions, can be chosen. Perhaps this will yet be done. That would be a good thing—for the purpose of citing these thirty-eight is to arouse a measure of interest and even a bit of action.

In each chapter, the thoughts of a scientist are juxtaposed against those of other scientists with related views on the same topic. In doing this, the author is fully conscious of the danger of changing the meaning of a passage by taking it out of its context. However, this danger is minimized by the fact that the selections were obtained through personal interviews, in which the true intent of a passage is more easily determined than if it were taken from a printed page.

Another hazard of the arrangement of the book is that of the possible overlap of ideas from one section to another. This was avoided wherever possible. But, on occasion, the development of a particular idea or the power of a well-chosen flow of words was considered more important than the avoidance of overlapping.

The marginal identifications of the contributors permit the reader to reconstruct individual interviews quite easily. The index is a further aid in this use of the book. In a sense, the reader thereby takes the place of the writer and shares the excitement and provocativeness of the personal encounters. New insights and stimulation of thought will grow out of such repeated readings of the comments of the individual scientists.

An instructive outcome of this procedure is the discovery that there are no standard sets of views on science and religion. That is, what a man thinks about the existence of God does not necessarily determine his view on the role of the church. This is precisely why the book is arranged the way it is. Rather than make the presentation disjointed, the technique achieves a correlating effect.

Of fundamental importance is the fact that no significant opinions have been omitted in order to give weight to a particular viewpoint. All relevant thoughts expressed by the contributors are recorded. Where deletions were made, the contributor either repeated himself or digressed into unrelated topics.

Quotations from the interviews are introduced and tied together by the author's comments, which are set in a contrasting typeface. They consist of questions from the interviews and ideas suggested by the quotations. This commentary has been kept to a minimum, its main purpose being to present the thoughts of the contributors in meaningful and logical sequence. It is unavoidable, of course, that the commentary as well as the choice of sequence of quotations represents an arbitrary judgment of sorts, but it is one which is necessary if the presentation is to have coherence.

The sequence of topics in the book is roughly the same as that followed in most of the interviews. Before the scientists speak out on the key questions of the survey, they discuss basic definitions of science and of God. This is exactly the kind of logical progression that many of the contributors stressed as being of fundamental importance. It will be noted, in fact, that virtually all the contributors expressed themselves on the "ground rule" questions in the opening three chapters, whereas many of them side-stepped some of the later topics. *The reader who is eager to get immediately to the more controversial parts of the book should start with Chapter III or IV and should then consult the background materials in the opening chapters at his leisure.*

The last chapter is the author's reaction to the study. This is not only his prerogative but also something that several contributors urged him to do. This closing chapter is not designed to lead the reader toward any specific conclusions. Rather, in keeping with the pervading purpose of the survey, it is meant to encourage him to take a fresh look at the concern of the scientific community for the welfare of the human spirit.

* * *

The author is deeply indebted to the contributors for their time and interest. He also owes a large debt to a number of other individuals who helped to make this book possible. The idea for the study grew out of suggestions by the Reverend Edward H. Stammel and the Reverend Roland H. A. Seboldt. The work would not have been possible without the help and encouragement of Herbert H. Kunmann, who implemented the necessary research and for whom the whole endeavor assumed the proportions of a vital mission. Charles and Phyllis Penaz have, for many years, contributed enthusiasm and materials to the author's books. Finally, and most important, the author's family provided the countless hours of necessary quietude and cooperation for the work, even during family vacations. To these, and to the many others who expressed their interest, the author extends his sincere thanks.

Contributing Scientists

(The position listed for each contributor was the one held by him at the time of the interview.)

DR. ROBERT A. ALBERTY
Dean, School of Science, Massachusetts Institute of Technology, Cambridge, Massachusetts.

DR. HUBERT N. ALYEA
Professor of Chemistry, Princeton University, Princeton, New Jersey.

"AN OXFORD SCIENTIST."
Professor at Oxford University, Oxford, England (anonymous by request).

DR. ARTHUR G. ANDERSON
Director of Research, International Business Machines Corporation, Yorktown Heights, New York.

DR. HANJOCHEM AUTRUM
Dean, Faculty of Sciences, University of Munich, Munich, Germany.

DR. GEORGE W. BEADLE
Director, Institute for Biomedical Research of the American Medical Association. Former president, University of Chicago, Chicago, Illinois. *Nobel Prize in physiology, 1958.*

ALF R. BJERCKE
President, Bjercke Paint Corporation, Oslo, Norway.

DR. MAX BORN
Professor Emeritus of Physics, Universities of Göttingen and Edinburgh, Bad Pyrmont, Germany. *Nobel Prize in physics, 1954.*

DR. HARVEY BROOKS
Dean, Division of Engineering and Applied Physics, Harvard University, Cambridge, Massachusetts.

PROF. STEPHEN S. DAVIS
Dean, School of Engineering and Architecture, Howard University, Washington, D.C.

DR. JULES C. DUCHESNE
Chairman, Department of Atomic and Molecular Physics, University of Liege, Liege, Belgium.

DR. FRIEDRICH EHRENBERGER
Analytical Chemist, Farbwerke Hoechst, Kelkheim, Germany.

DR. WERNER FORSSMANN
Head, Department of Surgery, Duesseldorf Evangelical Hospital, Duesseldorf, Germany. *Nobel Prize in medicine, 1956.*

DR. JOHN P. FRIEDRICH
Principal Chemist, USDA Northern Regional Research Laboratory, Peoria, Illinois.

DR. OLE KRISTOFFER GJØTTERUD
Professor of Physics, University of Oslo, Oslo, Norway.

DR. ARTHUR G. HANSEN
President, Purdue University, Lafayette, Indiana. Former Dean of Engineering and President, Georgia Institute of Technology.

DR. KRISTIAN HORN
Professor of Botany, University of Oslo, Oslo, Norway.

DR. J. ALLEN HYNEK
Director, Lindheimer Astronomical Research Center, Northwestern University, Evanston, Illinois.

DR. DAVID R. INGLIS
Senior Physicist, Argonne National Laboratory, Argonne, Illinois.

DR. M. JEUKEN, S.J.
Professor of Theoretical Biology, Leyden University, Leyden, Holland.

DR. ARTHUR B. KOMAR
Dean, Belfer Graduate School of Science, Yeshivah University, New York, New York.

DR. AUGUSTIN LOMBARD
Professor of Geology, Former Dean, Faculty of Natural Sciences, University of Geneva, Geneva, Switzerland.

DR. OLE M. LØNSJØ
Professor of Physics, University of Oslo, Oslo, Norway.

DR. MICHEL MANDEL
Professor of Physical Chemistry, Leyden University, Leyden, Holland.

DR. JACQUES E. PICCARD
Oceanographic Engineer and Consultant, Grumman Aircraft Engineering Corporation, Riviera Beach, Florida.

DR. MAGNUS PIHL
Professor of Physics, Former Dean, Faculty of Mathematics and Natural Science, University of Copenhagen, Copenhagen, Denmark.

DR. JAN H. RYDBERG
Head, Department of Nuclear Chemistry, Chalmers University of Technology, Gothenburg, Sweden.

DR. ROALD TANGEN
Dean, Faculty of Mathematics and Natural Sciences, University of Oslo, Oslo, Norway.

DR. RUDOLF TRÜMPY
Professor of Geology, Former Dean, School of Natural Science, Swiss Federal Institute of Technology, Zurich, Switzerland.

PROF. HARRY J. TURNER
Marine Biologist, Woods Hole Oceanographic Institution, Woods Hole, Massachusetts.

DR. JAN J. VAN IERSEL
Professor of Experimental Zoology, Leyden University, Leyden, Holland.

DR. BERNARD WALDMAN
Dean, College of Science, University of Notre Dame, Notre Dame, Indiana.

DR. KURT WALLENFELS
Director, Chemical Institute, University of Freiburg, Freiburg, Germany.

DR. WILHELM H. WESTPHAL
Professor Emeritus of Physics, Technical University of Berlin, Berlin, Germany.

DR. LEON J. F. WINAND
Dean, Faculty of Science, University of Liege, Liege, Belgium.

DR. GERHARD WOLF-HEIDEGGER
Professor of Anatomy, University of Basel, Basel, Switzerland.

DR. WILLIS G. WORCESTER
Dean, College of Engineering, Virginia Polytechnic Institute, Blacksburg, Virginia.

DR. KARL ZIEGLER
Director, Max Planck Institute for Coal Research, Muehlheim/Ruhr, Germany, *Nobel Prize in chemistry, 1963.*

1

Of Science and Scientists

When Is It Science?

In common parlance, to be "scientific" means to do a thorough and methodical piece of work. Any information that is categorized and assembled in a logical sequence is apt to be called a "science." The terms have become virtually synonymous with truth, and to be called "unscientific" is often more derogatory than to be labeled as stupid.

> *Science is a kind of sacred cow today. It is being* **Friedrich**
> *worshiped by the public.*

How does this image of science compare with a scientist's own definition and evaluation of his work? Strangely, the responses to this question were often the shortest of all.

> *Science is the search for truth and the explana-* **Friedrich**
> *tion of observed phenomena.*

> *Science is something that can be tested by experi-* **Alberty**
> *ment and abstract reasoning, such as mathematics*
> *provides, about which there isn't any argument.*

This last definition introduces a most important consideration, namely the interplay of science and mathematics. Mathematics implies definite rules and rigorous, sequential thinking. If the proper rules are not followed, a scientist will not call the endeavor scientific.

Hynek *Science might be called organized curiosity, a concerted attack on that which is knowable. I've often likened it to a sort of game. It has very definite rules. The reason that science has been as productive, materially, as it has is because these rules are so rigorous and because it has had the good sense to confine itself to things which are productive. It has played a superb game of tennis because it has stayed on the tennis court and didn't go wandering off on a hockey field or something. A person who is a good tennis player can also be a good golfer. But if he decides to keep his wrist action the same in tennis as he does in golf, he's going to be in trouble.*

Do rigorous rules make science cold and unemotional? No more so than tennis or golf, or any other game that is played according to rules. In fact, a good player needs imagination as well as skill if he is to excel. It is no different in science. The endless measuring and testing are motivated by a desire to know, a belief that the universe will yield answers.

Born *Five seconds before I made my discovery I didn't know what would happen.*

Gjøtterud *What is very specific to science is the way the questions are asked—a critical attitude, but also belief. I think that is very much forgotten. We are very dependent on having an idea. We must believe, in a sense, to get the force and strength to work out the answers. It's not as cold as a hypothesis. One must have an idea, a view, a perspective of where this is going. I feel that science is the process of asking questions and trying to answer them critically, but also with inspiration.*

2

> *The scientist has faith that the universe is poten-* **Hynek**
> *tially, publicly knowable, that there are no inside
> wires, not anything that is available to one person
> and not to another. This is an article of faith.*

To say that only scientists work in this way is perhaps too narrow. Surely many other areas of knowledge involve similar methods of investigation:

> *I would question whether there is a scientific* **Alyea**
> *method. It is the method that all research people,
> whether they are in history or economics or English,
> go into. It's a logic of collecting data and examining
> data and arriving at a conclusion from extrapolating
> those data into hypotheses. It's identified as the
> scientific method only because science has so few
> variables. It's so much simpler to see what the pro-
> cedure is. It's a kind of sleuthing in a logical way.*

Man has an insatiable desire to know. Does this urge have a divine origin? Some scientists think so:

> *God told man in the first pages of the Bible to* **Lønsjø**
> *subdue the world. That is what science has been
> doing and is continually doing.*

Perhaps the reason for the brief and almost reluctant definitions of science is that science is primarily doing. The thinking, the theorizing, the talking all have a single pur-pose: to pave the way for the actions by which the scientist tries to understand still another facet of the universe in which he lives.

> *Science is an experimental thing. Science without* **Waldman**
> *experiments is of no value. Foolishness comes out.
> If you have any thought about how things are, it is
> essential that you test them out against experience.
> If you're convinced that experiment doesn't verify
> what you're saying, you have to drop it.*

> *Science is what scientists do.* **Hynek**

3

How True Is a Fact?

In *The King and I*, the ruler of Siam finds the changing interpretation of truth "a puzzlement." He was brought up to believe that "what was so, was so; what was not, was not." As an adult, he finds that things are, at best, "nearly so."

Do scientists resemble the young king or the older one? How does a scientist view his own findings and those of fellow workers, both past and present?

Worcester   *I'm not going to jump off a cliff on the chance that the law of gravity won't work that particular time. This takes a little more faith than I can exhibit.*

This expression of confidence must not be misunderstood, however. Within the optimism of that statement is the important idea that scientific findings, including the law of gravity, are based on statistical evidence, on the observation of many isolated and independent occurrences. The certainty of a conclusion is entirely dependent on the nature and extent of the supporting data.

Friedrich   *Scientists are quite often misquoted in the area of certainty. I don't believe that anything is absolutely certain. Things are more or less certain depending upon the data which we have to support a given conclusion. If there is a sufficient amount of data supporting some conclusion, and no contradictory data, then we say with a certain degree of certainty that it is a true, reliable conclusion.*

Within this frame of reference, scientists deal confidently with their conclusions. They work with the optimistic assumption that science is systematically zeroing in on ultimate truths, even though these may remain forever out of sight.

An experimental scientific truth is something that **Mandel**
is found by using some kind of experimental tech-
nique which has its own limitations. These limita-
tions also limit the validity of the experimental
scientific truth. An improvement of the equipment
may challenge a scientific truth found previously. It
only means that the truth as found previously is
more limited than one thought at the moment. It
doesn't mean that it was necessarily wrong. No truth
which is accepted at a certain moment will become
completely without value. It may become more
limited, and be true only under certain well-defined
circumstances and conditions, but there isn't much
chance nowadays that truth which has been ac-
cepted on an experimental basis will be found later
on to be completely wrong.

The conclusions of science are never certain. It is **Lombard**
a process of evolution.

The word "truth" has many meanings. If you **Van Iersel**
mean by truth that science has relevant knowledge,
you may call scientific knowledge truthful, because
you can predict certain things with the aid of this
knowledge. It is relevant for your prediction. It is
quite difficult to give a general definition of truth. It
might be, as a good scientist, that you have to
change your view. But at the moment that you
make your prediction or give your theory, it is
truthful up to that time. Nobody knows what can
be discovered in the future. Nobody knows how our
notions have to be changed because of new investi-
gations. You may say it is relative truth.

Perhaps too many science courses still resemble the
training of the young king in this respect. If so, they are a
disservice to science.

When I was a student, my professor stood before **Alyea**
me and said, with all the dignity and solemnity of

5

the Pope in issuing a religious dogma: "Gentlemen, matter can be neither created nor destroyed." You say this to a high school student today and he'll laugh and say, "Haven't you ever heard of $E=mc^2$ and how Einstein predicted how energy would come off when matter is destroyed; and how also man has generated matter from energy?" Now I have sense enough not to stand before my class and say, "Gentlemen, matter and energy cannot be destroyed, but they can be interconverted," because possibly my grandson might stand before his class and say, "Granddad was all wrong. What he really should have said was, 'Matter, energy, and blurps cannot be destroyed.'" You see, blurps haven't been discovered yet. I lecture to my students for a whole week about fundamental laws, and between "laws" and "fundamental" I put a great, big question mark. For a whole week we examine that question mark. As that question mark looms bigger and bigger, our understanding becomes greater and greater. It isn't that we're confused. We're getting closer to reality as refinements are added to natural laws. We're more accurate now than we were two hundred years ago. But we still haven't reached the ultimate. Our entire approach to reality is asymptotic. We're getting closer and closer to the absolute.

Gjøtterud   *It's a heavy responsibility for the teacher not only to teach dogmatic facts without discussion, but really to show the students the worth of the problems. One should stress the questions and problems that are not solved, so that the young people can be stimulated. I think there is a tendency in science teaching to be terribly dogmatic.*

So things become increasingly certain, but they are never absolutely so. A scientist must be able to live and work in a limbo in which it is entirely possible and even necessary to learn something without understanding it, to

6

know the what but not the why. Scientists are concerned about the misconceptions of the layman on this point.

Alberty

I am not one of those who think in terms of science dealing with truth. We always deal with a kind of approximation. There isn't anything very absolute about scientific theory or fact. Science is an organized body of knowledge which works. When scientists calculate that they can make an H-bomb, it works out that they can make an H-bomb. If they say that they can send men to the moon, they can send men to the moon. But that doesn't confer any kind of absolutism on the basis on which they made the calculations. They're still approximations. We'll still learn more about those things. But we have the ability to do certain things that we can continually test. They're reproducible and dependable. But they're not understood. Most scientists don't seek an understanding that's absolute. Their understanding is of an operational nature. The ability to control and do is a sort of substitute for understanding. They don't know what understanding is and they certainly don't know what truth is. In their personal lives they have some concept of understanding and truth, but the use of these words is very much exaggerated in science.

Hansen

Laymen are often awed by the accomplishments of science and they feel that scientists know the why as well as the what. There is perhaps great confusion on this point. Consequently, one puts the scientist in an esteemed position—often without good cause. What really is it that a scientist attempts to do? Quite simply, as I understand it, a scientist is seeking what might be called verifiable truth. That is, he is trying to comprehend the way nature works and, in doing that, formulates hypotheses or suggests laws which by themselves are not absolute, but are really relative to the state of knowledge at a

7

given time. They are as meaningful as he is able to observe and measure quantities that relate to these hypotheses and laws in the course of his investigation of nature. A scientist becomes a great scientist when the hypotheses that he sets forth encompass a greater range of phenomena than perhaps that stated by any scientist before him. This was indeed true of Albert Einstein who, in fact, extended the laws of Newton to the point where they could explain many more natural phenomena than Newton was able to do within the context of his formulation of natural laws. This does not mean that there is more truth in one formulation than in another one. It merely means that one has a more complete explanation of that which is observed.

Waldman *Science never really answers why. It answers how. Why do we have gravitation? No scientist has ever answered that question. I don't believe we're any nearer to that than we were fifty years ago. We accept the fact that there is gravitation. Then we decide the manner in which it will act. Knowing this, we explain all sorts of events that happen, both on the earth and off the earth. If one didn't completely understand Newton's law of gravitation, obviously we couldn't send a spaceship to the moon. We understand things and we use them, but we do not know why. We don't know why there is electricity. Many scientists believe they can solve these problems, but to my knowledge no one has made any real progress.*

How often does the march of science result in a complete turnabout in fundamental concepts? Are we, in some cases, zeroing in on myths? Scientists admit this possibility, but with considerable caution:

Alberty *Science has a certain amount of dogma in it. But it can always be questioned, it can always be over-*

thrown. If they decide it's wrong, they get rid of it just like that. It's a changing part of a changing world. They don't feel that science depends upon these things being maintained. They know that these things are probably wrong and will certainly be replaced. They are convenient now, but may not be useful next week or ten years from now. But they don't maintain that science will collapse if people quit believing this. They know that science will go on when people quit believing it, and it will be better science because something else will come along that they are willing to believe in. The evolution of science has to be accomplished without overthrowing very much. New theories tend to contain what is good about the old theories. You don't throw away what's good.

Physics can give you the attitude that you can't believe in anything which should be considered as an absolute value. You have to recognize that it is necessary to revise even your most fundamental beliefs in this world. The fundamental assumptions that physicists at the turn of the century thought to be true to all eternity have been shown not to be valid. We have learned that we should hesitate very much to claim that this or that truth is absolute.   **Pihl**

Turnabouts in scientific "truth" may even be a good omen:

There are always turnabouts in science. If there weren't turnabouts, scientists wouldn't be doing a good job, since this would probably mean that they were much too conservative. If science were too conservative it would not be progressing at the rate that it is today. We have to make mistakes, we have to reach conclusions that are going to turn out to be wrong in the future in order to have progress. If science would wait until the degree of certainty of   **Friedrich** *its conclusions were so ironclad that they couldn't be overthrown, we wouldn't see the progress that we have seen in the field.*

Piccard *Our earth way of thinking may change as we explore outer space.*

Some see an importance in the changing conclusions of science that reaches far beyond the laboratory. Science cannot isolate itself from society or from its responsibility toward people. Changing "truths" have spurred rather than slackened the pace of science. What is this saying to man and his problems?

Pihl *It has been necessary to revise the deepest assumptions which we formerly made about our knowledge of nature. This is not only a revision resulting from ordinary development, but we have seen in relativity theory and also in the development of the atomic theory and quantum mechanics that, in order to master these things, it is necessary to give up even the most fundamental ideas, the most fundamental assumptions. This is of very great importance for the influence of science on society. In order to cope with the very difficult problems with which we are faced nowadays in mastering our society, and in mastering the conflicts and tensions between groups and society and between nations, it may be necessary to change the most fundamental ideas about our position as human beings, of our understanding of our human situation.*

So perhaps the term "fact" should not be used in connection with science, at least not in the sense of the young king. Then what should one say? Try this:

Alyea *Say not "It is the truth," but "So it seems to me to be as I now see the thing I think I see."*

Or this:

10

OF SCIENCE AND SCIENTISTS

The more we know about the universe, in a way,   **Alberty**
*the more we don't know about it. There is an
increasing mystery about the whole thing. Every
time a scientist makes a discovery, he realizes that
there are ten more things he doesn't know. Science
has a kind of open-mindedness. You never converge
down on something but tend more to open up more
possibilities. The space program opens up a lot of
questions about the moon and planets and even
about the earth itself which people didn't think of
asking before.*

Or, more philosophically:

The position of the real scientist today is that of   **Duchesne**
*Newton when he said that we are like children
playing on the beach before the infinite ocean of
truth.*

What Is a Scientist?

Scientists are often caricatured as bespectacled, balding,
paunchy eggheads, dour of countenance, draped in over-
sized white coats, and weighed down with profundities
that have little bearing on the joys and woes of the average
human being. How much of this picture is correct? Do
certain personal attributes really incline a person toward a
scientific career, or is it the other way round?

Candid photos of the scientists interviewed for this
book would quickly dispel the idea that you can pick a scientist out of a crowd by his unique physical appearance.
However, there are several mental qualities that are considered by scientists themselves to be important to success
in the field. One of them is objectivity:

The primary prerequisite for being a good scien-   **Friedrich**
*tist is to be objective. This is difficult for any human
being. For some it's impossible. It's impossible for
anyone to be completely objective. In order to evaluate the results of your work and formulate ideas*

11

based on this evaluation, you have to be objective. You can't afford preconceived ideas and you have to be open-minded.

Open-mindedness is virtually forced upon the scientist by the nature of his work and especially by an examination of the recent history of science.

Gjøtterud
The scientist must always ask questions about his own method and his conclusions.

Komar
After having gone through two scientific revolutions since 1900 (quantum theory and relativity theory), most physicists have become shockproof and they realize that they are now entering into a realm where they have no intuition going for them. They really are open-minded. A good scientist is so completely open-minded that, in the words of Einstein, he doesn't let his left hand know what his right hand is doing. Einstein's philosophical attitude was diametrically opposed to the concept of a priori probability in the universe, which came up in the context of quantum theory. What he objected to in quantum theory was really a priori probabilities, not just probability based on insufficient knowledge of the details. It was pointed out to Einstein that he was the one who introduced a priori probabilities in physics. He said he was aware of that, but he was forced to do it by the nature of the phenomena he was investigating. Although he introduced it, he was disturbed by it. To the end of his life, he never liked it and didn't know what to do about it, because apparently nature is that way. If the phenomenon you are investigating forces you in a certain direction, even in violation of your intuition or philosophy, as a scientist you're obliged to go in that direction. A good scientist has to be open-minded about everything.

In a way, open-mindedness is a somewhat passive trait. Imbue it with a bit of action and it can be called skepticism. This can be exciting.

It's no fun if you're not skeptical.　　　　　　　　**Alyea**

Does all this open-mindedness, skepticism, and relative truth make scientists humble? Unfortunately, not always.

A scientist must be skeptical, especially toward 　**Trümpy**
his own work. As people, most scientists are con-
ceited. You can be conceited and skeptical at the
same time. The two do not rule each other out
completely. Quite a lot of scientists have a dogmatic
approach to science. This is very bad.

Science is not dogmatic. Many scientists are. The 　**Brooks**
social system of science prevents the dogmatism of
scientists from being counterproductive.

We teach our science students that humility and a 　**Hynek**
lack of a know-it-all attitude are essential. Unfortu-
nately, there are some scientists who are so com-
pletely human that when they get to be, let us say,
Nobel Prize winners or in very exalted positions,
they tend to forget this simple precept and get
rather egocentric about the whole thing and feel that
they are the final arbiters. History has time and
again proven them wrong.

It is the drawback of the science of our time that 　**Lombard**
it is perfectly satisfied with what science can grasp
and doesn't bother with what it cannot grasp. That
will be the great criticism a hundred years from
now. It will be considered the big mistake of our
time to have thought that we could reason out
religious questions with a purely scientific mind or
background. They will laugh at that and will say it is
a kind of Middle Ages, how these people of our time
were perfectly satisfied with their techniques, sci-

13

ence, discoveries, and never bothered with what was left to be explored. Science is not humble enough.

On the positive side, a scientific background can develop a self-confidence that transfers into other areas of living.

Alberty *You will find many scientists who haven't had formal training, but who regard themselves as experts about what the country should do about its economy or what we should be doing about our cities or black people. They feel that a person who thinks and takes advantage of the opportunities he has to learn through people and reading has a right to feel that he can have opinions which are worth considering. That comes a little bit from a scientist's self-confidence. He is even working in areas where he hasn't had training in a formal sense. He has to pick it up himself. That's a large part of what graduate work is. All scientists have this ability to quite a remarkable degree as compared to the general public—the ability to change fields, to learn something new, to have the self-confidence to do it.*

Nevertheless, it is humility that is singled out as perhaps the most important single trait of a successful scientist.

Alyea *The greatest scientists I've known are also the humblest scientists I've known.*

Davis *The greatest men are the most humble men. This has come about because of their realization of how little man really knows. I think this has always been the case. The more scientific we become the more we become aware of how little we know and how much there is to learn. This is true not only of science. Anyone who attempts to explore truth eventually reaches a stage where he realizes how insignificant man is in the total universe.*

Hansen *If anything great can be attributed to Einstein, it's his perpetual reiteration of the point of humil-*

ity, that he said he knew so little even though he was recognized as a great man.

Is humility a cause or an effect of scientific work? Can science turn arrogant men into humble ones?

Science has become more modest because of modern discoveries. **Duchesne**

Scientists should take very seriously what they are doing, but they should not take themselves too seriously. Science is not a play anymore. It's matured. It's responsible for changing the world. **Gjøtterud**

The really great men, the men who have made the major contributions to physics, are usually very humble. It's the fellow who's kind of fighting for acclaim, trying to climb up the ladder, who is not humble. Physics is no different from anything else in the world. Scientists are always people, and as people they're no different from people who are in business or people who are in the army or people anywhere. So there are scientists who climb on somebody else and who'll step on this man's head and shoulders as they go up the ladder. These guys usually aren't too humble. They're usually very brash and very sure of what they're doing and how they've solved all the problems. But the people who make the major contributions and the major breakthroughs are remarkably humble. **Waldman**

When we realize how much we don't know, and when in the course of research each discovery results in many new questions, you almost have to be humble because you realize how inadequate you are. The further you go and the longer you've been in it, the more you realize this. You have to be able to live with defeat and apparent failure, because research is only about ten percent fruitful. This doesn't mean that one out of ten things you try is going to **Friedrich**

15

work, however. You might be unfortunate, and after several years of work in which you feel you haven't accomplished anything it's easy to get discouraged. If you have that type of personality, you wouldn't be a good scientist.

In the final analysis, it may be necessary in some cases to distinguish the arrogance of the man from the humility of his work.

Brooks *Science is modest. Scientists aren't. It takes a great deal of egotism to be a good scientist. Science is very competitive and the judgments of scientists on each other are extremely harsh. It takes a fairly thick skin to be a scientist and even a certain a-mount of intellectual arrogance. But that doesn't mean that science as a social institution is intellectu-ally arrogant. That's a hard distinction for people to understand. The personality requirements for sci-ence tend to foster arrogance among individual sci-entists.*

For some, the outcome of this effort is something of a split personality, a double life:

Alberty *A scientist is aware of how little he knows. But this doesn't necessarily transfer into his personal life. He can be very humble in saying that there is a lot he doesn't understand, but he might be, in his personal relations, in your judgment and mine, an aggressive, egocentric person.*

As in any other field, many leaders of the scientific community have the traits that make for public promi-nence.

Alberty *One type of scientist is exactly the same kind of person who becomes a millionaire in industry. He is aggressive, hard-working, and has his eye on big things. He may be single-minded. In a sense, he is a*

√

businessman. I have dozens of friends on the faculty who operate research programs that cost a million dollars a year. They have to work for it and know people. They have to get bills passed by the Congress. They have to compete with the best people in other universities in their own field for that money. These are not quiet, mousy types. They're pushy and aggressive, but also charming. They're exactly the same kind of people that you would find as presidents of corporations. They're also extremely articulate. They write and speak well. People like them and like to work for them. Of course, I am talking about the leaders.

Aside from this leadership segment, however, scientists tend to speak of themselves as introspective and even seclusive.

There is a high correlation between scientific in- **Brooks**
terests and an introverted personality. On the other hand, it is not so much introverted as it is inner-directed.

Scientists, as a class, tend to be more introverted **Friedrich**
than other people, but I don't know why. The layman would call them "different." They are independent and sometimes appear to be almost bull-headed in all their philosophies.

Scientists and engineers are introverts. They take **Davis**
things very, very seriously. They are concerned about problems like religion, but they don't express it. Their thinking is inward. The engineer is a factual person. He likes to think in terms of black and white. This is typical of most scientists. The person in nonscientific areas is very articulate, extroverted, and a little more aware of the consequences than is the scientist. It is very easy for me to make a decision, whereas I find that it is very difficult for these others to make decisions. They will belabor a

17

*problem and belabor it and still have no answer.
Sometimes this method has the advantage of arriving
at a compromise at which the scientist will not
arrive. It might be a little more human.*

Perhaps this introversion is responsible for the reputation of many scientists as nonjoiners. They often find
organizational procedures boring and even unnecessary.

Turner   *Church membership and attendance in our scientific community is quite low compared with that of
other people. Very often they will contribute because their wives push them into it. They find it
relatively meaningless. Scientists are mavericks.
They are not joiners, for the most part, and nonscientists are the reverse. Not only do the scientists
stay out of the church for the most part, but they
also seldom join the Kiwanis or Rotary clubs and
other fraternal orders. They do have their scientific
societies, but meetings are generally annual events
where the members can present papers for the enlightenment (or boredom) of the audience and listen
to (or avoid) learned discussions of erudite verbal
haze. Business meetings generally command a very
poor attendance. On the other hand, the pews of the
local ecclesiastical shops teem with members of all
kinds of clubs, of which the church seems to be one.
If you ever attended one of the weekly meetings of
the Kiwanis Club, as I have many times, to give a
speech, you probably observed the following:*

*The meeting place is a local eatery with a room
set aside for meetings. The members all assemble
with well-washed faces, wearing oversize badges in-
scribed with first names. At the appointed time, all
file to the meeting room and stand back of the
chairs, with the speaker on the right of El Presi-
dente. The Lord's Prayer is then recited in somewhat of a monotone mumble, the flag is saluted
with the hand over the heart, and then a dissonant*

version of "America" is sung to the accompaniment of an out-of-tune piano played by a member whose ideas of harmony rival those of Hindemith. Following that, the president whangs the gong and everyone pitches into an inferior supper. The president then whangs the gong, and an interminable parliamentary session goes on with all kinds of inconsequential argument. When it comes time for the speaker, nobody gives a damn and neither does the speaker.

Apparently, this is the sort of thing that people like, because it happens every week. Scientists, on the other hand, find it sickening. To the scientist, church services have somewhat of a similarity to the above, but the music is generally better and the setting more restful. To a scientist, the church is largely one more social organization which may be about as unattractive as any other club.

If you're a scientist, you are not dependent upon the direct relationship with all the other people. Consequently, you can be a little less hypocritical and you can say, "I'm not interested in religion. I have my beliefs. I just simply will not join or get involved seriously in any organized church." Nobody will say anything to you. Your livelihood and your job are not in any way endangered. But if you are a businessman in town, if you're selling something to somebody, if you're a dentist, a doctor, a lawyer, or anything else, it is to your advantage to be a member of the proper congregation. **Waldman**

This is not to say that the personality traits of scientists run counter to the requirements of religious faith. It merely points up a distinction between church attendance and religious conviction.

Faith is not too different from a part of the regular life of the scientist. If he didn't have faith **Alberty**

19

that experiments can be reproduced and that the human mind is competent to learn more and that somehow things can be rationalized, he wouldn't go into the lab. All those acts of faith are necessary to the scientist. Maybe he doesn't look at it as faith, but it really is. This doesn't necessarily make him accept things easily, but it's wrong to think that he operates by some kind of cold, calculating logic. Good scientists are highly intuitive and don't follow rigid logic. They have a great feel for things, as opposed to a detailed mastery. We present it to our students as if it were all coldly factual, but that's not the way the frontier of science is.

Autrum   *In the last century, science has become more humble. Originally, it felt that it can do everything, that it can know the infinite and the unknowable. Modern science has become more modest when it considers its methods and knows that it cannot give a universal view of man. Man is more than an object that works and perceives with rational methods. It is easier for a scientist to believe in God today than it was fifty years ago because science has become more humble and recognizes its boundaries.*

A scientist is, after all, still a human being, with all the qualities and needs that man is heir to. Science does not make the whole man.

Friedrich   *A scientist must be able to reason from the unknown to the known and to evaluate data critically. He has to be coldly objective in his work, but he can't be coldly objective in his associations with other people, or he's going to end up needing mental treatment.*

"Oxford"   *A scientist is just an ordinary man who has been trained to think in a particular way.*

2

Staying on the Playing Field

Where Are the Limits?

The methods and attitudes of the scientist produce results. In the relatively short time since the birth of modern science in the fifteenth century, man's grasp of the universe has grown at a logarithmic rate. So has the range of creature comforts that this increasing grasp makes possible. So impressive and pleasant are many of these technological developments, in fact, that many people today see the major role of science as the alleviation of man's problems and the furnishing of ever more and better implements of pleasure.

A cloud hangs over this idyllic scene, however—a cloud that has become mushroom-shaped in our time. What of a science that produces tanks as well as tractors, ecological imbalance as well as insecticides, the ultimate weapon alongside the instruments for enrichment and prolongation of life? Is science potentially limitless in its paradoxical onrush?

> *Science has no limits. There are no questions it should not approach. I am extremely optimistic about the possibilities of science.* **Rydberg**

> *The scope of our experience grows, since experience always points to new questions that must be* **Westphal**

21

pursued in order to gather new experiences. Such experiences are always true. With the proliferation of means with which we can put questions to nature, the scope of areas in which questions can be asked also widens. The microcosm is very typical. First chemistry discovered the atom. Then it went from the atom to the nucleus, and then to elementary particles. We are probably not finished yet.

Wallenfels *There is nothing off limits, where a scientist is not to look in. Each problem is a problem for the scientist.*

Efforts to establish limits have not fared well:

Worcester *The trouble with questions about the boundaries of science is that, if you answer them, you're bound to be shown a liar a few years later.*

Anderson *We keep penetrating what other people have said are the limits. It's not clear how far the limits will go. We're constantly finding ways in which to eliminate or modify the assumptions on which we predict the limits. Every time in the past that someone has decided that certain questions are not legitimate questions for science, they've been wrong. Should there be a human determination that certain areas of human understanding should be self-forbidden under the interpretation that those areas of human intellect are the prerogative of "God"? My answer is that by the very statement of the question you prove that it's ridiculous. Let me give some reasons why. Let's suppose that the area is biology. Can you assure me that those areas aren't essentially going to make the difference, in the next fifty years, between whether or not any man lives on the earth?*

On the other hand, there is a clear realization that the search for reality is strewn with obstacles. Examples can be drawn from every field.

22

The possibility to solve problems is very different   **Wallenfels**
*in different fields. For the natural scientist, the
biggest unsolved problem is differentiation, the
development of a fertilized egg to a whole organism,
in which all the organization of the finished organism is prescribed in the nucleic acids of the fertilized
egg. We have some ideas now, but the whole understanding of this problem is at a very low level.*

There is always a point beyond which science   **Beadle**
*cannot go. It's now quite clear to many people in
science that as one pushes back in organic evolution
toward simpler and simpler forms one finally faces
the question of whether a system is living or non-
living. Enzymes have been synthesized. Enzymes are
characteristic of all living systems. Biologically
active nucleic acids will surely be synthesized in the
future. Are these molecules living or are they non-
living? The question has little meaning, for there is
no longer a sharp line between living and nonliving.
All elements and all molecules are in principle capable
of evolving from hydrogen. The ultimate question then becomes, "Whence came the hydrogen?"
Science has no answer.*

Do these obstacles have common origins? Perhaps so.
The scientific method, by definition, imposes some definite limits.

Science is limited only by our ability to design   **Friedrich**
experiments to test the theories which we may have.

I have an instinctive feeling that there are some   **Worcester**
*things that we will never fully understand. There are
places where the scientific method breaks down.*

The domain of the truths of 1900 is not as broad   **Komar**
*as the people then thought it was. Where they ex-
trapolated from their experiments to their theories,
it is as true today as it was then. It's just that there*

23

was a realm where because of their technology they were unable to perform any experiments, so they extrapolated their theory into that realm for want of anything better. What we've learned since then is that this is an improper extrapolation, that when you get into new realms you get a new series of experiments which deviate from the naive extrapolation. Where they did their work they were perfectly correct. It's where they tried to guess that they went wrong.

Gjøtterud   *We accept a certain set of methods, and by these methods we are able to ask a certain set of questions. This questioning is a very important thing. But to make the step to redefine reality to what we can reach by these methods, that is to narrow down reality. This is what many people do.*

Obstacles also lie within the scientist himself—his finite ability to perceive, to formulate, to understand.

Horn   *Men are limited, both physically and mentally. We have a rational ability. We have to take one attitude toward what we can achieve (things that are individually controllable), and we ought to have another attitude toward what I would call our pure ideas. Science can tell us where we reach the limits. Outside these limits men can use their fantasies and ideas as they like, in full freedom.*

Winand   *An isolated fact is something that is well established in its limits. The fact is that your tape recorder is working. We explain that in a way now. Maybe we could explain it better as a fact tomorrow or next year. A fact is a fact, but the explanation of the fact varies very widely as science goes on.*

Autrum   *Science is defined as the rationalization of the physical world. That is, we examine the physical world with the methods of perceiving reason. We* *know the limits of reason. Science has its limits where we can no longer examine, with reason, the objectively given subjects and can no longer examine ideographic and nomological questions with its restricted methods.*

With our limited perception we can know nothing of what is beyond our spiritual boundaries, beyond the limits of our knowledge and our senses. Man can never understand everything. For example, our ear can detect frequencies between sixteen and twenty thousand per second. I have a little whistle with which I call my dog. It makes thirty-five thousand vibrations per second, which I no longer hear, but which I could record electrically. It lies beyond the reach of my senses.

Forssmann

Since the Renaissance, scientific research has tried to extend the scope of the senses by means of accessory materials. The telescope and the microscope were the first breakthroughs of man beyond his bodily senses. This has progressed, so that in modern physics we think of our environment in mathematical terms that few people can understand. Through this, much has been established as truth. Whether everything is correct, we cannot control. In nuclear physics, new working hypotheses are constantly set up, overthrown, and improved through new circumstances. These are all things that are not personally perceptible for us.

How correct are these individual thought models? When I consider a highly developed sense organ, such as the eye or the ear, which are both evolutionary descendants of the brain, then its performance is limited. We see accurately only within the narrow range of the visible spectrum. The sharp perception of color is limited to a small optimal range. The closer we get to the limits of vision, the less distinct it becomes and the less certain the ability to distinguish becomes. Similarly, optimal performances are also established in dynamics. For example, when I hear low tones and come to the lowest limit of audibility, I can barely distinguish between tones. At the upper limits of audibility, I hear only very shrill sounds which I cannot distinguish either. But now something else plays a role, and that is dynamics. When I hear something that is very loud, then precision also diminishes, just as when I hear something very faint. When I see something that is too bright or too dim, precision again diminishes.

I often ask myself, "How far do we go in our thought models and with our mathematical constructions toward the limits where it becomes unclear?" They are, after all, products of our senses and mind. This can be carried over into every single area. Take moral sensitivity, for example, which is very narrow for some. For others it is very broad and sensitive. Whatever is beyond is uncertain.

Mandel *There are phenomena that science can't understand yet, but that doesn't mean that they fall beyond the scope of science.*

The scientist is not to be misunderstood, therefore, when he speaks of the unlimited possibilities of his work. He not only recognizes the existence of boundaries but emphasizes them with an urgency that may sound strange to the layman of the Space Age.

Alberty *If we devoted all our efforts to feeding people in such a way that it excluded art and music and what we would call abstract science, then it would be a less human world.*

Waldman *We usually start the first physics course with a discussion of "Why?" and "How?" and things like that, and just point out to them that we're just not going to be able to answer these questions, and maybe they can get the answers in a metaphysics course under the philosophy department.*

Science cannot deal directly with questions of value. Science can have something to say about describing values and describing the relationships between values and describing the values of different groups of people and why they are held. But the method of science is not designed to make value judgments. **Brooks**

We have to make a distinction between what we think is a fact (if we do so and so, we see these phenomena) and what we think of as the philosophical, the ontological question. We are just as far from the ontological questions as we have always been. **Gjøtterud**

The limits of science are given by its assumptions. You must know what science assumes in order to be sure about the limits of the conclusions you can draw. From a practical point of view, I don't think there is anything in the world which can't be handled in a scientific way. It is a way of looking at reality, but it is just one way of looking at it, determined by its assumptions. One can also look at it from an aesthetic point of view, from an ethical one, and from a religious one. I don't think that one can be a complete man by being scientific only. I see no reason to deny certain experiences and say that they are not true. **Van Iersel**

Questions of ethics and metaphysics are completely tangential to science. It's the belief that the world of man can be ordered methodically and scientifically and can be categorized that is wrong. That's where the error enters. The world of man is not quite the same as the abstract and objective world of science. There is the element of consciousness, free will, and emotions, which science can shed some light on but can never, never determine values for. Science can clear the air on what questions are properly ethical considerations. However, once you **Komar**

27

determine what is the realm of ethics, then science has no more to say, because it cannot tell what your attitude toward something ought to be.

What concerns me and frightens me is that, having won this great victory for knowledge and against mysticism and gobbledygook, science now stands astride the field and tends to become a new religion. Science was once a very progressive force. Now it's becoming a very dangerous force, because it is a very dehumanizing force. There is no compassion in science. There are just cold facts. There is an important role to be played for compassion, for human frailties, for human wants and needs, which have nothing to do with science except in a very general and vague way. Science is not capable of emotional demands.

Hynek *There are so many questions that are no-no's. It's like having a deck of cards and dealing them out. If you're applying the rules of bridge, you're playing bridge. But you can use that deck of cards for many other games. Science has just as many rigid rules as bridge has. There is the scientific method, what data are admissible, how one makes observations, under what conditions you can reject observations. It's a very hard and fast set of rules.*

Science does not deal with everything. It deals only with things that are amenable to the scientific method. It is completely lost when questions of revelation come up or questions of ultimate truth or absolute values. Science has no way of testing this. Unless there is some means of making it publicly available, it is not in the playing field of science. This point is frequently missed, that science has a playing field which may be quite different from other playing fields. Imagine the embarrassment of a golfer showing up on a tennis court with his golf clubs. Tennis has rules and golf has rules. A scientist frequently feels very lost when he shows up in a theologian's study. They're not talking the same language.

The failure to recognize the boundaries drawn in these statements can lead to grotesque miscarriages of the scientific method:

The one dangerous thing where I have seen mis- **Komar**
uses and abuses in the name of science is where
people feel that to find scientific truth is so impor-
tant that the sacrifice of certain individuals is per-
missible, such as doing experiments on children in
schools to see how they're motivated. Will they
learn better if you're strict with them? What if you
beat them? Will they learn better or worse? Or, to
carry it to a more grotesque extreme, take the pseudo-
scientific experiments in the Nazi concentration
camps. One has to have some human sense of values.
A computer would find no objection to these tests.
After all, the scientific method says that the only
way to find out the response to certain types of
actions is to perform the actions and find the re-
sponse. It's this parody of science that I've seen
certain people really advocate and feel fully justified
in doing. Norbert Wiener discussed the danger of
letting the scientific attitude rule completely. He
pointed out that if you present a supercomputer
with the problem of how to achieve universal peace,
it will give the very obvious, machine-like, mathe-
matical solution: exterminate people.

Do the Limits Point to Religion?

Man was actively religious long before he was methodically scientific. When science came, did it fill a void in man's montage of needs or did it, in progressive fashion, take the place of religion in man's arsenal for living a complete life? Will the role of religious faith in modern thinking rapidly diminish as science advances? Or are the

29

boundaries of science eloquently saying that the converse is true—that religious faith is the logical complement of the scientific method and that science is really establishing an ever-increasing need for spiritual awareness?

Tangen *The humbleness of science is extremely important. The layman thinks that we know the truth. We will never take that word in our mouths. In fact, the truth has no meaning. When you take the limitations of your work inside a certain sphere and the truth of all these things is outside, then you are approaching the problems of religion.*

Worcester *There are people who feel that everything can be explained on a purely scientific basis, but all of them eventually run into unanswerable questions, questions of their own origin, of the earth's origin, of their ultimate fate, which simply can't be answered on the basis of any currently known scientific method or knowledge.*

Inglis *Science cannot deal with every question. This is the point at which many scientists begin to have thoughts that are akin to thoughts of religion. The problems of the outer bounds of the universe and the inner bounds of the atom are so profound and awe-inspiring. It seems clear that science gives us an understanding that is only a connection between things and not an understanding of the ultimate origin or cause. We keep coming up against this feeling that science can't go the whole way.*

Autrum *Man needs more than science can give him. But whether he turns to religion for it or to some other philosophy is up to him. The thought methods of science must be clearly defined. It must be made very clear that science is only one side of human activity and culture. It is not everything. There is something besides the rational treatment of nature, something that cannot be measured with dimensions* *and numbers. Science, in trying to find universal laws, will find its boundaries. There is the right of the individual, which is not in contradiction to science. That is where religion begins.*

Good scientists are pretty deep thinkers and the fact that a scientist realizes that the number of questions he has grows faster than the number of answers he can produce leads him toward religion. There definitely has to be a sort of boundary between science and faith, or else faith would certainly have to be discarded. There are certain areas which are not testable by the scientific method, and religion is one of these areas. **Friedrich**

Science cannot speak out on in-between, subjective phenomena. It cannot set values. It does not make religion unnecessary. On the contrary, a precisely understood science leaves every freedom for a religion. **Autrum**

Man reaches a certain point in his life where he feels that science falls short in satisfying some of his needs. Therefore, the only thing he has remaining to fall upon is religion. Religion fills a need that is very difficult to explain but nevertheless exists. **Davis**

Religious men speak of faith. So do scientists in talking about science. There is a similarity, and a difference, in their concepts of faith.

The source of inspiration, before expressing hypotheses, is of the same sort as the source of the inspiration which determines artistic creation. They proceed in similar ways. It is a manner of grasping the universe with the skin, if you will. Science, as well as religion, arises from inspiration which belongs to the irrational part of man. **Duchesne**

There are infinitely many questions that science cannot deal with. This is where questions of faith **Westphal**

31

come in. They do not concern science. This must be left up to the individual. Faith is a very dangerous word. The writer of the letter to the Hebrews said, "Faith is the substance of things hoped for, the evidence of things not seen." Physics cannot deal with this kind of faith. When I say, "I believe," it can mean I believe in something. That is the believing of religion. When I say, "I believe that we will have bad weather tomorrow," this has nothing to do with religious faith. In religion, believing means to consider something to be absolutely true. In the other sense, it means to hold it as probable. The latter leads to scientific hypotheses which are not proved yet but which present a possibility. Scientific faith means to consider something as plausible.

Religious faith is a highly individualistic matter. It is perhaps the most intensely personal experience of man. How, then, can it be merely a logical conclusion arising from a set of rigorous scientific postulates? With scientists, as with all men, religious faith is an individual experience.

Van Iersel   *What he thinks of it, the scientific way of formulating reality, can give a man an aesthetic notion: it is a nice theory, it is simple, it is elegant, etc. I realize that there is a step from an aesthetic notion to a religious one. You can't say that one leads to the other automatically.*

Wolf-Heidegger   *One can and will and must come to a limit where one cannot go any farther. The place of this limit varies. It moves somewhat over the centuries and is different for different areas. It is very different for biology than for physics and different for physics than for chemistry, but it is my belief that there is a limit beyond which you cannot go with knowledge and understanding and spiritual comprehension. That is very clear. At that moment you can either fall into skepticism or begin to believe. It is up to the individual.*

It is self-evident that individual choices—leaps of faith—vary widely. But the right and necessity to make the leap are recognized by many of today's scientists. They distinguish sharply between the realm of science and the realm of religion.

I would consider science and religion to be two   **Hansen**
very distinct human activities. I would put the theologian in somewhat the same category as a philosopher in that he is a person who is primarily value-oriented. That is to say, he is a seeker of truth relative to values relating to human life. In this context, he is different from the scientist, who is concerned with the physical universe, stating hypotheses, and working with the idea that any hypothesis must be capable of verification by standard techniques of scientific inquiry. The scientist's results must ultimately be quantifiable and, as such, are distinct from the results that are formulated by the philosopher or the theologian. The latter are not concerned with quantifiable things as much as with qualities. When a scientist goes beyond verifiable hypotheses and speculates on ultimate reality, he leaves his role as a scientist and becomes, at best, a scientific philosopher. Correspondingly, when a theologian speculates on matters that are related to our physical universe, he steps out of his role as a theologian.

Religion is illogical but not irrational. Science is   **Van Iersel**
strictly logical, but the rational is anything the human mind produces. The irrational includes those notions in my brain which are not subjected to criticism, are not made clear, are not made very conscious, have no reasoning in them. One of the expressions of man is religion. In this sense, you can say religion has a genetic basis. But from a scientific point of view, of course, I can never say that there are religious genes.

33

Lombard *I feel better when I make a strong frontier between science and religion. There is a part of religious thought which has to be detached from science. The ideas and experiences we have every day in our lives come from other sources of information. They involve other ways of thinking and reasoning than are applied in science.*

Alyea *Science is* adequate *in the physical world. Contact with the physical world gives me increased confidence in science, in the adequacy of science. But science is also* inadequate. *The other side of the picture is that there are other things that I intuitively realize science cannot measure. For those things that I cannot measure I intuitively turn to something other than science, my religion. If I were not a scientist, I would not have that intense faith in the dogmas of science. They are dogmas. All of science is bound up in these dogmas, and they have given us the scientific structure and superstructure. In the same way, I turn to my religion, and I have faith that the superstructure of religion, based on intuitive feeling, is equally secure.*

Jeuken *We have in our mind several levels of thought: science, philosophy, religion. Each level has its own kind of thinking and kind of certainty that you can reach. For instance, in answering the question "What is life?", science will answer in terms of life phenomena (moving, assimilating, propagating, respiring). But this does not answer the question. It only tells how life appears to you. The question is a philosophic one. The starting point of philosophy is always self-reflection. In religion, you start by listening to revelation. Then you can say Yes or No. It is more than knowledge. It is surrender.*

It is totally wrong when philosophers or archaeologists prescribe a certain definite conclusion to reach on the scientific level. The reverse is also wrong. Each level of thinking has to remain in its own region with its own kind of arguments and conclusions. But we can't divide ourselves. There must be a synthesis of the three levels. You must make a distinction, but not a separation. After you analyze, you must make a synthesis.

I believe that you can never approach basic religious questions with scientific knowledge. We can, at best, establish how meaningful many things are and what is beyond man. With man, much is meaningless. Even though we know the meaning of nature better than was imagined formerly, we are no further along in our religious views.

Wolf-Heidegger

I cannot accept the optimistic view that religious questions will eventually not be necessary. Our technical abilities are growing continuously (transplants, geophysics, space travel), but we are still far from knowing why, where from, and where to. Man lives his seventy or more years, and what is that in relation to the whole of existence? Nothing. This important realization is not a sign of depression but of realism. It is simply so.

It may very well be, as was thought in the Middle Ages, that there are certain mysteries that will always be known only to God, and that man will never know them.

Hynek

Perhaps the scientist has an obligation toward his fellow-man in this respect that needs to be brought out. If so, it is certainly not a question of science versus religion, but rather of scientists assuming their roles as leaders in the scientific-religious milieu of our time.

I consider it as the absolute duty of a practicing scientist, irrespective of the field he is working in, to analyze the questions of religion, God, the world, his assignment, etc. If he doesn't do this, his conclu-

Wolf-Heidegger

sions will merely support his preconceptions. The result may be positive or negative or somewhere between, but the analysis must be undertaken by the spiritually active person. Although it sounds socially arrogant, this is an obligation that the scientist has over against the person who is not active spiritually. Among the latter there are many who analyze these questions on the basis of some inner problems or with reference to some inner compulsion, and the like. I don't want to make an arrogant distinction between academicians and simple people, but I want to emphasize that one group has the obligation to make the analysis while with the other group it is optional. This means that, since I believe that I must do my duty, I have made the analysis also.

As part of such an analysis, many scientists point out that religion has been an integral part of every culture, irrespective of its degree of sophistication. This amounts from the scientist's viewpoint to a proof that religion is necessary to man's welfare and that it has an important role to play also in keeping modern man on an even keel. To some, however, the demands and rewards of science play a religious role.

Beadle *Religion is an essential part of human culture. It is necessary. It has survival value. I believe that is why all cultures have developed religions. Religions provide something necessary for man that science and other areas do not.*

Rydberg *Religion keeps people together in a society. You can see how important religion is in Israel in building up the state. Young people are not strong believers in religion, but religion keeps them together, in a way, and makes them stronger.*

Bjercke *You need religion to face what we are facing today. If we look a little bit beyond our noses, we*

36

can see all sorts of conflicts coming. How can we face them without religion?

The church is necessary for a great number of people, and I won't meddle with their ideas, but for myself I could easily do without it. I came to this view largely through my own studies. I wanted to become a minister when I was young and so I studied theology and church history. I got completely disgusted with it. **Trümpy**

Stability is important to people, for the masses need something solid to hold to. Scientists are perhaps less likely to need this. They often find they have alternatives. **Beadle**

You must have something in common with your neighbors in order to live together with them. It may be religion but it can also be other things. Scientists have a sect of their own. They may be believers or unbelievers, but it's the science which keeps them together. It's an outlook on life. You may be religious and I am not, but as scientists we understand each other. **Rydberg**

Are Limits Restrictive?

Granted that science and religion represent distinguishably different areas of concern about reality, do scientists purposely separate them in their lives? Is such a separation even possible?

The question is complex. There is no doubt that a clear separation can and must be made in dealing with specific investigations. This can be done without compromising either the scientific or the religious commitments of the investigator, although it may take on the aspects of a double standard to the casual observer.

Science is not an all-encompassing view of the world. That is to say, it doesn't have to be that in **Brooks** *the point of view of the individual scientist. He can work in a sort of limited domain for his interests and not have it incompatible with his religious beliefs. That's not quite the same thing as saying, though, that the total world view of science, regarded as a social institution, is completely compatible with the world view of religion as a social institution.*

Beadle *I suspect creative scientists are likely to put science and religion in separate categories. Insofar as they do, religion doesn't greatly influence their science.*

Pihl *A man can keep his religious beliefs separate from his science. Human beings can separate contradictory states in the mind, which may be a good thing.*

Wolf-Heidegger *A scientist with religious beliefs can be just as good as another. This belongs to the freedom of the spirit. It doesn't have the slightest connection with one's work. The limitations of science are encountered by both the believer and the unbeliever. One will interpret it one way and the other one another way. The work up to these limits is exactly the same.*

Alyea *Our life is a joint effort. On the one side is the physical world which the scientists are investigating. At the same time, there is the entirely separate spiritual world, which the ecclesiastic can interpret better than the average citizen, just as the scientist can interpret science better than the average citizen.*

Turner *A great many people can split their personalities so that they look at their religious views one way and their scientific views in another way. I know three or four rather devout scientists, but they seem to be able to split their personality off so that in one room they can inquire into natural phenomena and in the other room they proceed with their worship.*

Scientists work merely because they're interested in coming up with something new. Many of them dissociate themselves, for the most part, from the moral and ethical aspects of these developments. **Davis**

It does not make a person a better or a worse scientist if he is a Christian. Investigating reality in a scientific way can give a scientist a feeling of admiration, religious admiration. It could be a motive for his work. If the study of science destroys religious faith, then it may be that it was not the right faith. Faith means quite a lot of question marks, maybe more question marks than certainties. Strictly speaking, science cannot strengthen faith, because faith can only be strengthened in religion itself. **Van Iersel**

A man can be a good Christian and a good scientist—or a bad one. **Autrum**

My experience is that you can be a Christian and a scientist, or an atheist and a scientist too. **Lønsjø**

The church sees from me only my church tax, which is high enough to pay two ministers. But I still retain my membership. These questions have nothing to do with my activities as a scientist. I did not become more or less religious because of any scientific experiences. If I were in a different profession, my church activities would not be a bit different. **Ziegler**

You won't find many scientists who become believers through the practice of science. Most people are believers by education. Even if they get more involved in science by themselves and start to think about it, they still can't reject that part which they have by education, and then they try to separate that part of their beliefs and that part which concerns their activities. I have friends who are considered to be very good scientists and who are very **Mandel**

39

religious people, not by accident only, but by conviction. There must be some kind of split personality if you are at the same time active in science and believe. They don't let the two interfere in their minds.

Friedrich *I don't know whether anybody is objective enough to know whether he has a split personality or not. I don't feel that I have one. In the final analysis, a person doesn't know himself very well at all.*

What one man may call a separation, however, another may not. Neither will an individual investigator be able to bring off the same degree of detachment in each investigation or from one day to the next. Man is a total being, and the compartmentalizations that learning requires are, in a way, at variance with the nature of man.

Consciously or unconsciously, then, religious views often affect the science of scientists. The effect can be negative.

Rydberg *Belief in God can be a hindrance to a scientist if he believes so strongly in God that he cannot understand those who do not believe. This may be a state of mind which causes him also to believe in his scientific results in such a way that he cannot accept that they are wrong or that other people have found other results.*

Hansen *Anybody can be colored by his beliefs and opinions. There is the old cliché about the older scientist telling the young researcher, "Always be careful that you do not discover what you want to discover." A good scientist tries to be as coldly objective as possible. Anything that has a strong emotional tinge to it, such as a very strong religious belief, could ultimately have an impact on that man as a scientific investigator. One might take, as a very simple case in point, a laboratory group that was concerned with the creation of life. A religious individual would say that this is not in the province of science. Only God can create life. Therefore, what's being done here is not scientifically sound. He would tend to shy away from giving a scientific evaluation of the results of experiments.*

Some say that, when a swallow builds a certain type of nest to take care of its young, it is because of an instinct given to the bird by God. I wouldn't say this is less true than any scientific speculation about the type of background. The difference is that if you give the first explanation you exclude the possibility of making an investigation of how it really is. The other type of man says, "I think that this protein, which is produced by the prescription of a certain number of genes in the chromosomes of these birds, makes a sequence of signals on a certain surface in the brain of the bird, from which the bird can read off which course he has to take, how long one string has to be in one direction, when he has to make a knot," etc. But I wouldn't say that this type of explanation is any better than the other, because one hasn't made any good experiments to explain this. But if you give this explanation you can say, "I will try to find out. For example, I can take a small piece from the brain of a spider and transfer it to another spider and see if he makes the network of the first spider." To say that God informed the egg what to do when it is a living bird and the bird now acts according to this inborn prescription which was given him by God and is given him constantly by God, this makes one happy and all things are finished.

Wallenfels

To be a good Christian and a good scientist is an almost insoluble conflict. Scientists are trained to be critical. When I told one of my teachers, "I believe that," he would say, "Faith is not involved here."

Forssmann

41

Theology is based on faith, and that is to some extent quite comfortable. When they don't get any farther with reason and criticism, then they can always refer to faith. When you are in a profession that is not based on faith, this will also affect all your other thinking. Our brain is not that flexible.

Friedrich   *The scientist who runs out of ideas for answering the questions he has set out to answer, and says that it is something for God to answer, is either lazy or else doesn't have the ability he should have. A good scientist will not say such a thing.*

This may be the reason why many scientists are not actively religious. But it is important to remember that the emphasis is on "actively."

Waldman   *Most of the physical scientists I know, particularly those who have achieved some reasonable degree of success, are usually not particularly active in religion. This does not mean they're dis-believers. It's just that they're inactive. When a scientist gets a Ph.D., he is about twenty-seven or twenty-nine years old. The first thing he has to do is get his reputation. He goes to some institution on a post-doctoral program and he has to work just as hard as ever, because in a two-year appointment he wants to publish something. So he works like a madman. Then he becomes an assistant professor at a university. Once again he is back on the 16-hour grind until he gets promoted to tenure, which is associate professor. By this time he is about thirty-three or thirty-four years old, he's raising a family, and he's got into a habit, a habit which is not so easy to break. So what does this fellow do? He continues his life. His wife is trained and everything is set. The net result is that he just somehow never gets out there and says, "I will devote my evenings to do a little* *work for the church and join one of the discussion groups."*

This is the average man. Now there comes a time when that changes, however. When he is forty or forty-five years old, when he's a full professor and the children are no longer running around screaming in the house, then maybe he has a little time to do this. This is when you find a lot more activity.

I have met very few scientists whom I would **Pihl**
really call deeply religious in the sense that they state explicitly that they belong to a well-defined religion.

There are some hundreds of scientists comprising **Turner**
this community, and I think it would be safe to say that the majority could be classified as unbelievers, at least in the orthodox sense. The unbelieving situation is not a binding force, as the individuals do not assemble in the name of nonbelief, do not perform any group activities, and do not generally even discuss it. There are apparently a few more or less devout individuals, and in one of the institutions an appreciable fraction of Reform and Conservative Jews, but everyone minds his or her business in regard to religion and everybody is happy.

Religious feeling cannot, of course, be categorized into a single set of beliefs, even in juxtaposition to science. There may be as many religions as there are people, which is really consistent with a proper definition of religion.

Many individual scientists find that certain aspects of their religious convictions influence their science quite positively.

A person who is religious should be a better **Friedrich**
researcher than one who is not religious. A Christian feels a responsibility toward his job which a non-Christian may not feel. He feels that it is important

43

that he do a good job, that he is serving man and through serving man is serving God in his work, and that therefore he should do the best job he can do. A nonreligious individual might do just enough to get by or might have no qualms about the type of work he does.

Alyea   *Faith gives you a sort of inner quietness that, I think, would also give you a willingness to be resigned to failures in your work. Nine out of every ten experiments in the laboratory lead you either to defeat or into new fields that you never envisioned before. The test of an optimist is to be handed lemons all day and then go home at night and make lemonade. The inner composure that faith in the spiritual gives you can be transferred to science.*

Wallenfels   *Each human being is religious in a certain way. There is no nonreligious man, unless he is very, very stupid or is not mentally healthy. If such a normal reaction is not there, I would be very careful about having a collaborator like this, because I wouldn't be sure about the truth of his findings. Without the possibility to think about deeper questions or to have such questions, a man of this type would react in a dangerous way. If he has the possibility to produce nice results just by writing and not by experiment, and to modify experiments in order to give a good result as viewed by the professor or the scientific community, then I would say this is a dangerous man and I wouldn't like him as a collaborator.*

Komar   *The morality and judgment of individual scientists have to be guided by ethical considerations. A scientist has to think about the implications of what he is doing and not just be a cog in a wheel. Where religions enter is to bring these ethical considerations to the fore.*

Science requires a lot of moral and ethical personal properties of a man. If he is religious, these may be easier for him to acquire. He must have great patience and humbleness, which he can learn in religion. Scientists today are often just the opposite.

Born

I'm not sure that the scientific community has, in the past, given as much thought to the moral implications as it should have. We are looking at it more now, primarily because we feel a little guilty because of what our young people are doing. We're beginning to look at ourselves.

Davis

It can also be a two-way street. Many find that scientific training and thinking strengthen religious beliefs—or at least distill them.

My belief in the Christian ethic has been reinforced by my thinking as a scientist. I believe that the Christian ethic is the only way, in the long run, through which the human race can maintain a viable society.

Brooks

A lot of scientists feel that one cannot think scientifically and at the same time believe in things like the resurrection and immortality, but I don't think this affects my ability to perform as a scientist at all. I don't mean to imply that I completely divorce my scientific background and training from my religious life. I see a certain blending of the two which just happens. You can't avoid it. Science is a part of me just like religion is. This is probably why I am a little more critical of my religion and of what I have been taught in the past. I question it. I try to look at it critically and objectively to see whether I had a good reason for accepting what I was taught. But I don't feel that this affects my scientific work. Perhaps the converse is true. Science somewhat affects my religious life.

Friedrich

45

Anderson   *The contributions to an understanding of the development of religion from archaeology are well worth a substantial investment by the churches. From archaeology, anthropology, and other sciences the church can learn a lot about the mood of the times under which it grew and the degree to which the customs which have become traditional were part of the evolving social fabric. The church can learn to understand itself tremendously better from these sciences. I haven't seen any great effort to do so, however.*

Jeuken   *Science furnishes the subject matter for moral thinking. Science gives inspirations but not arguments. For example, modern biology has given to the theologians new subject matter: artificial insemination, hygienics, that kind of thing. Science gives them a field.*

Komar   *The nature of the exploration of archaeology clearly has nothing to do with the mystical or the metaphysical. It simply has to do with the factual. Did the events described in the Bible occur?*

Alyea   *Spiritual matters are matters of intuition and belief. Science and religion go together in this sense. The scientific method is terribly important in interpreting the Bible, showing where things were misinterpreted—that the earth is not flat, for example—that we took on faith five hundred years ago and did not question. It does not make the Lord any less magnificent if we can date when the earth was formed.*

Van Iersel   *Science should say explicitly to the church that science has its own world. The church should combine its own conclusions, which must be religious, with scientific notions. The church should not limit scientific research. Application is another thing. The* *man who applies science acts as a human, with ethics. Ethics are influenced by religion. Ethics are not illogical. It can be studied by the church with a good, scientific approach.*

The progress of science can give direction to theologians to become better theologians. They are not to mingle themselves with scientific efforts. Science has given inspiration to theologians to think about the real *revelation point of the Bible.* **Jeuken**

The world will be healthier when we realize that science provides a strength for a very valuable type of religion that has some of the two-thousand-year-old mysticism removed from it and that is focused on the needs of the twentieth century. There is something about the human spirit that is inseparable from religion. It exists. It has sprung up in every primitive society in one form or another for individuals and societies, filling this human need. But it will have to be in conformity with what we know about nature, about the handiwork of the creator. The church has shown a great appreciation of the wonders of science and has drawn strength for religious convictions from the wonders of the universe that were discovered by science. **Inglis**

Could it be, then, that neither science nor religion can independently arrive at an adequate picture of man in his universe today, and that both must be blended in order to approach reality?

With some scientists it is not science or *religion, it's both religion* and *science extended to make a totally new concept.* **Hynek**
We're somewhat in the situation of a man who wants to build a beautiful mansion in which to live. He wants a library, music room, swimming pool, master bedroom, nice dining room, kitchen, etc. But as he looks around he sees that he has just a limited

47

number of bricks. What, then, does he do? Does he decide just to build a tiny little hovel in which to live? I say No. I think I've solved that problem this way: I use imaginary bricks. I go ahead and build my mansion and live in it, with one rule—that I will never substitute an imaginary brick if a real brick is available. The real bricks I equate with scientific facts.

It's perfectly all right to build your mansion of many, many rooms and live in it, because we have to live as rich a life as possible. If I can lead a richer life if I believe in angels, in reincarnation, in life after death, in ultimate values, etc., then why not? I can live in a more luxurious house and live a richer, more meaningful life than I would if I just stuck to "Water is H_2O," and refused to believe in angels unless I could prove that they have a certain chemical composition. That would be too confining. I refuse to be so confined. But that in no way lessens my respect for science, because the real bricks that science has produced are extremely valuable. Within that framework, I also allow myself all sorts of imaginary bricks. The danger is that, if you should let this preoccupation with imaginary rooms in your mansion interfere with what we do know about reality, then you're in trouble.

Alyea *With the help of spiritual interpreters, a mutual growth of spiritual and physical understanding will get us closer and closer to what reality in both of these is.*

Waldman *The thing that bothers me personally the most is watching the people in the community and seeing them take such a serious interest in religion and the practice of religion on Sundays and then not apply one iota of this to their daily lives, to business. I find that the ethics of most businessmen is sometimes questionable. They separate business and reli-*

gion. Maybe it's the same thing as separating science and religion.

It should not be surprising, therefore, that many scientists are actively religious. In some cases, the involvement is much greater than outward appearance would indicate.

Most scientists, if you really open them up, are religious.   **Davis**

It is fantastic how active the members of our chemistry department have been in church affairs. It's a very false impression that scientists are, in general, atheists.   **Alyea**

It's been my experience that members of congregations and officers of the churches I've attended have been pretty well sprinkled with people from the scientific and technical areas. We have a good many engineers here who served on the boards of a number of churches. We have several who have acted as lay ministers. Some of them are trained as ministers.   **Worcester**

There are two reasons why scientists seem less religious today: 1) they are more humble and do not publicize their views as much; 2) people don't speak as openly to each other as before, especially about religion; perhaps it is an inheritance from totalitarian regimes, where you had to atone for your views and concur with ideas of which you were not convinced yourself.   **Ehrenberger**

I haven't worked with very many people who have no faith, no belief in God to fall back on.   **Worcester**

Most scientists are religious men.   **Jeuken**

This attitude seems to be on the increase, at least in some areas.

Van Iersel   *It is important that laymen should realize that scientists are not such atheists as, let us say, they were some time ago. Perhaps the scientists who were not atheists just did not say anything. It is more acceptable among scientists in Europe today to speak about religion.*

But, in the final analysis, how widespread is the religious involvement of scientists today? The very wording of the question makes a satisfactory answer difficult, to say nothing of the problem of obtaining adequate data. Yet there is a universal curiosity about the relative number of "religious" scientists when compared with, say, lawyers or bankers. Such figures seem to have great meaning in a day of polls and computerized conclusions.

Lacking an applicable poll for evidence, what do scientists think of themselves as a group when it comes to religion?

Autrum   *I don't believe that the percentage of believing scientists is any different from that in other professions.*

Brooks   *Many people who write about science and religion pick out scientists who are very religious and generalize from this. I think that, on a statistical basis, highly educated people are probably less interested in and less dependent on religious beliefs than other people. I don't think this is more common among scientists than it is among other people of equivalent education.*

Lønsjø   *There is just as great a percentage of physicists here who take an active part in church work as there is in the population in the region where I live.*

Worcester   *I think the percentage of scientists who are believers is at least as high as it is in other professions. Many ministers, in fact, have a background in electrical engineering or some other branch of engineer-*

ing. Electrical engineering seems to be an area that generates a great many ministers. I don't really know why. I know quite a number of ministers who started out as electrical engineers.

3

Defining God

In drawing the line between science and religion, on which side of the line does the scientist place the existence of God? Is the idea of a supernatural being an entirely religious concept, or can the instruments of science detect evidences of the existence of a creating or intervening power in the universe?

The question has several aspects. Religion is defined, on the one hand, as the worship of a deity. If science leaves room for religion, is it thereby implying the existence of a God? On the other hand, even some religious leaders have raised the cry, "God is dead."

How much can science say about the health of God, past, present, or future?

Is God Provable?

A large number of replies on the scientific approach to the existence of God were direct and unequivocal:

Winand   *I don't think science can prove or disprove the existence of God. It's not a matter of science. It's a matter of faith.*

Autrum   *There is no possibility for science to define the necessity for God. But there is also no possibility to deny him.*

A good, objective scientist who is unexposed to religion isn't going to say that there is no God any more than he is going to say that there is a God. He feels that there is no proof for it and no proof against it. **Friedrich**

The existence of God is entirely unattackable for the scientist. God is, in and of himself, not representable for our mind and our senses. **Forssmann**

The scientific method cannot deal with the existence of God. The method was not established for this purpose. We cannot require God to be rational. If there is a God, he is what he is. **Westphal**

The existence of God is outside the province of science. I well remember Enrico Fermi once saying that science has no way of demonstrating that there is or is not a creator, or that there might or might not have been one in the past. **Beadle**

Science leaves the question of God completely open. Science has no right to judge it. **Born**

God is not observable. He is not within the scope of proof. Knowledge of God is qualitative. You can't quantify it into pieces of knowledge. **Van Iersel**

It is impossible to determine whether there is a God. **Trümpy**

The concept of God is not definitive enough to be subject to proof. It is a subjective feeling in the heart of every man. **Inglis**

Nothing that I have learned about science so far has disproved to me that there is a God. **Bjercke**

The existence of God is not a scientific question. **Alberty**

There has been some misdirected teaching on this point.

Anderson   *I attended a religious college, in which I found that we were trying to prove very many things that, as far as I'm concerned, defy proof. I really concluded that I could think about it and didn't have to take their interpretation. I went through the usual epistemology and logic courses and had the usual proofs for the existence of a God. In my judgment, they were all fundamentally dependent upon prior assumptions that God existed.*

Science deals with clearly stated hypotheses and precisely defined terms. For many scientists, the concept of God has not been defined in terms that are reachable by the scientific method. This may not be a shortcoming of the definitions—it may be the very essence of the matter.

Mandel   *God is an idea, an abstract construction. If you define him in such a way that belongs to natural phenomena, then I would say it falls within the scope of science. If you give a negative definition of God, even then one could make the ideas which lead to the abstract construction of God also fall within the scope of science.*

Wallenfels   *The existence of God is not a question that you can ask because first you have to define God, and there you have the first difficulty. The definition of God must be different for each individual. It cannot be prescribed.*

Komar   *You can't prove the existence of something you haven't been prepared to define properly. If you just use a three-letter word, you can prove that the three-letter word exists simply by writing it down. Normally, when the man in the street uses the word "God" in the ordinary English usage, what I assume he means is some independent volition which has an independent will, that can make decisions, that has whims, that can be appealed to to change his mind* *and to do favors for one. In science, one plays games with words and takes words in nonstandard meanings, in which case all bets are off.*

The laws of nature are so wonderful and compli- **Tangen**
cated that you can just as easily say that they were made by God. You can say that the will of God is the same as the laws of nature. But when you speak of a God of ethics and morals, you are in a completely different field.

Are the manifestations of God continually changing? Then the definition cannot be static either.

Many scientists still have the idea that when a **Hynek**
theologian speaks of God he is still speaking of the interventive old man that sits up high in the clouds and, at his pleasure, decides to interfere in the running of the universe. This, I'm told by theologians, is long gone. The concept of God is evolving, as well as man.

Recent concepts of God are not within the prov- **Hansen**
ince of science. This is not to say that early and primitive concepts of God were not capable of scientific investigation. As a case in point, it was believed in times past that God resided in a tree, and that by placing offerings before the tree, man could influence natural phenomena such as the growing of crops or the making of rain. But this sort of concept can easily be checked out by the scientific method and one can make tests to see whether or not offerings placed before trees did result in some way in observed events. We have, of course, come a long way since those primitive times, and man has certainly acquired a more sophisticated concept of the nature of God.

One tries, over and over again, to make a picture **Forssmann**
of God for oneself. The difficulty is that many

55

scientific things have developed so rapidly in recent years that our childhood representation of God can no longer be made to harmonize with them.

Is this tantamount to saying that God is whatever man wants to make of him?

Horn   *We have no proof that the concept of God is more than an idea. Man can have psychological experiences about being converted, so that he thinks he believes there is a God.*

Does Science Need a God?

Modern scientific treatises rarely mention the concept of God in any form. This seems to imply that the acceptance of a deity, either as a prime cause or as a living force, is clearly not a prerequisite to meaningful endeavor in the sciences.

Mandel   *The existence of natural laws does not imply the existence of a higher order. What is higher order? Higher order than what? The existence of matter does not make a prime cause necessary. If that were the case, then one could ask the same question about the prime cause. The question can even be put, "Is there an origin of matter?" Why should there be an origin of something? The asking of questions of origins is already an indication of something. It may already be a belief.*

Komar   *The concept of God is completely meaningless and useless in connection with the origin of the universe, because it's just pushing it back one step further. If you say, first of all, "Who started it all?" and then you say that God did, then you're begging the question, because the next obvious question is "Who started God, and where did he come from?" Then the reply is, "He is eternal." Then why not have the universe be eternal and be done with it. It* *explains nothing. To give it a word is to cover up your ignorance.*

In none of the fields of nuclear chemistry have I **Rydberg**
found any reason to say that this is done by God. We can take two substances today and add them together and they will reproduce, which means that we will have life. It is not necessary to have a God to touch that and blow his breath over it. When you divide these substances, there is no life anymore. Biochemistry has revealed enormous things about the human mind. We have drugs that can change the mind of a person. How is God involved in that? Would it change God by taking hashish?

It is easy to say that everything must have started and that God started it. I don't believe this. Things can have continued for infinity. Indefinite time, as such, may be an absolute thing. We can have a universe which is indefinite, where matter is spread rather evenly from the beginning of time. There is no reason for a God in this. Suppose that the universe started with one atom in each cubic meter. Why should God make that kind of universe? It contracted, a nuclear reaction starts building up, elements build up, and finally we have man running around on this small earth in this big universe and talking about God. This is a very complicated and most unexpected way for a God to act. I can't find any reason for it.

If you ask the question, "Who created the Big **Wallenfels**
Bang?" the next question is "Who created the creator?" If religion says that God created the world, intelligent children will ask, "Who created God?"

There is no reason, more than a semantic one, for **Brooks**
equating orderliness in the universe with the existence of God, unless you define God as the principle of orderliness. I don't think there is any evidence in

57

the natural world which gives any indication of the existence of an intervening God. The question of a prime cause is not a very interesting one. It is largely a semantic question.

Turner   *The more you find out how things work, the less the need for the magical resources of the deity. Suppose the process of aging becomes understood, so that it can be arrested and man can become potentially immortal (except for fatal accidents), what will that do to theology? Faith in an unseen supreme personal being, magic, and supernatural phenomena do not register with the scientist.*

The divorcement of God from the scientific method is not necessarily an act of atheism or agnosticism, however. It merely indicates that man is capable of explaining natural phenomena without introducing a concept that is tangential to his investigations.

Hynek   *When Laplace had finished his three huge volumes on celestial mechanics, he presented them to Napoleon. Napoleon very hastily thumbed through them and said, "I see here no mention of God." Laplace said, "Sire, I have no need of that hypothesis." What he meant, and it is not necessarily sacrilegious, is that in order to explain the motion of the planets and stars and moon, etc., all he needed was the law of gravitation and the laws of motion and some knowledge of calculus.*

Van Iersel   *We can explain phenomena without God. It's a bad thing to introduce God as an explanation in science. This weakens religion, because it makes it less necessary to use God as science progresses.*

Proof is one thing. Feeling is another. A scientist is subject to both, and it has already been pointed out that the scientific method employs both. As quick as scientists are to rule out God as a provable entity, many of them are just as eager to point out that science does not debar the strong feeling that the universe must be under supernatural control. Many are convinced that scientists are in a better position to recognize the necessity for a God than are nonscientists.

There is a purpose to life beyond probability. All the results of evolution must have a purpose. **Piccard**

I have great respect for whoever set up the laws of nature. I feel a little sorry for the skeptic. Let him tell me what came before God. I don't think he knows. It is one of those things that will remain forever unprovable. I don't think the universe is eternal. **Worcester**

Proving the existence of God is not a question on the scientific level. Nevertheless, there can be hints from one level to another level. **Jeuken**

The thing that's most interesting to a scientist is that you find this tremendous order in nature. It's more than just a coincidence. As science progresses, one sees more and more the order in nature. Things are not just completely happenstance. Therefore you would be more inclined to believe that there is some master plan. **Waldman**

We have certain inklings that there is some sense in the evolution of the earth and humanity. It is sometimes very difficult to understand it without supposing some sense behind it. **Trümpy**

You really come down to a position, as a scientist, that this is a pretty tremendous universe, one that shows a fantastic degree of order and common sense. If somebody did plan it, it surely evolved beautifully. You have a choice between there being a God and calling evolution God. Evolution is still a very, very powerful force. So even if the choice was **Anderson** *that evolution is God, then it's still very active. On the other hand, if God set up the evolutionary forces, it is still very active also. An idea lives if it is effective, and the ideas of order and beauty are certainly effective.*

Piccard *The principle of uncertainty proves that God can exist. The idea of probability involves a freedom of choice. The more we learn, the less we know we know. We never have the final explanation. We can always ask "Why?" as children do. The last "Why?" can be God.*

Forssmann *The fact that scientific laws are valid throughout the universe is certainly an indication that the material world has a common spiritual basis. This basis is the creation or is concerned with a creation.*

"Oxford" *It is a very attractive belief that, because there is so much order in nature, there must be some designer, some artist who thought it all up. But this is a belief, not an argument. You can't go from one to the other.*

Inglis *The concept of God is the lack of capability to go further and the untold wonder of it all, the way things click together so beautifully. You just have a feeling it can't come out of nothing and be so wonderful by chance. There must be something purposeful beyond what we know. It's not a matter of proving God's existence but of defining what it is that makes you feel this way. There's something awesome and mysterious about the origin of things, the nature of things, the elegance of physical laws that we formulate but don't understand. It gives me and many of my fellow scientists a feeling that, although we can't formulate what it is, there is something grand and beautiful in the way of a cause of the whole thing that can't be fathomed and that is very close to what the layman thinks of in terms* *of God, at least the layman who doesn't put arms and legs on his God.*

We see a lot of the wondrous works of the creator of the universe that are invisible to the people who don't have our kind of microscopic or macroscopic vision. We're not lacking for wondrous works of the creator in man-size things either. Look at the biology of any part of the human body or even the tiniest living mite. There's more wonder there than can last one man for his lifetime.

Who made the Big Bang? You need someone who did this. The human brain is limited to a certain type of thinking and nobody can be sure that there are not other possibilities. For example, nobody can really imagine a four-dimensional room. The human brain is not able to see a room with more than three dimensions. This is the definition of a room for a normal thinking man. But every mathematician will see that this is ridiculous. Why not have four, five, six, or any number of dimensions in a room? **Wallenfels**

Science can say there are laws in nature and somebody must have made them. Or perhaps it's not right to say that some person has made them. I always used to think that if something exists it must be made. If there is such an idea as God, it would be working every minute, everywhere in the world. **Born**

Many people find, as they examine the universe, more and more of its beauties. It gives them more of a feeling that there is a God than if they don't see this beauty and system and how remarkable it is. This aspect of science often keeps God alive for scientists when he might have disappeared from their lives. This is not a proof, however. It is an intuitive feeling, a supportive kind of feeling that this universe and this life must mean something, otherwise it wouldn't be so wonderful. To the scien- **Alberty** *tist it is, in its physical aspect, even more remarkable than it is to the layman, because he sees the details, he sees the interaction between molecules, he sees how a living, thinking, feeling person is made up of molecules and how these actions are all interrelated. He sees how the stars are born and die and how this universe may have formed. These things make him think it's really very remarkable. That isn't to say that scientists are terribly religious as a group, but certainly this aspect of God is evident to them, what a remarkable and mysterious universe it is.*

Worcester   *Many times the scientific method yields a large statistical probability that something is true without a final, absolute proof. A great many thoughtful scientists and engineers seem to feel that everything can be proved by the scientific method and that you don't really need a God in order to explain everything. But there is one little thing I always get hung up on and I think others do too. We say that everything works according to certain natural laws and overlook the fact that some kind of intellect had to set up the laws.*

Alyea   *Science strengthens my religion. The more contact I have with the physical world, the more I believe in the reality of God.*

Are even scientists sometimes too arrogant to see a religious leaning in their work?

Ehrenberger   *The search for new knowledge in nature should lead to God. What prevents man in general from finding God is perhaps the overestimation of his ego, his great delusion.*

Is the existence of God more obvious in some sciences than in others? Or is it entirely a matter for the individual scientist to experience, no matter what his field?

You will find that among physical scientists there **Turner**
is a greater tendency to look at an intelligence
governing the order in the universe than among
biological scientists. But theirs is a fairly simple
order. Biological scientists are dealing with a much
higher order of complexity. They will be a little
more skeptical. Unified religion is not really mean-
ingful to the average biologist, although the physical
scientist, seeing some kind of order in the universe,
likes to ascribe it to some kind of intelligence. The
physical scientist has a very simple kind of science.
Even Einstein's $E=mc^2$ is a simple equation that I
can sit down and solve with a slide rule. The bio-
logical scientist is dealing with very complex chemi-
cal equations that are almost beyond his under-
standing. For example, the human brain can be
likened to a digital computer. In twelve hundred
cubic centimeters it has a capacity for accumulating
ten billion bits of information. You run into num-
bers that are much too large to understand.

When you discover how intricate and complicated **Winand**
things are in physics, it's impossible to have a con-
cept of all of nature only through theoretical phys-
ics. Something simpler and more powerful than the
human mind should exist that is the origin of this
thing.

In all times of natural science, one has had some **Wallenfels**
type of Godlike activity. Maxwell, one of the first
accurate theoretical physicists, produced the "de-
mon" that moves around and takes over the organi-
zation of certain problems at a certain moment. The
same is true for newer physics. In modern theoreti-
cal physics you have the uncertainty principle of
Heisenberg which is founded on the difficulty to
give precise answers to questions about the exact
movement of the electron. This is developed to the
opinion that nearly all physical events which are

known to us are purely statistical, not absolute, and have no longer any value when you go to a single atom. Heisenberg has also had the opinion, from time to time, that certain "demons" are at work which prescribe in certain cases what the electron has to do.

Hynek　　*I really know very few scientists who have told me out and out that they were atheists. I do know many astronomers who definitely are not atheists. They have too much of a respect for the vastness of the universe to just feel that mankind represents the highest intelligence in the universe. It's cosmically provincial to think that, and an astronomer is certainly in a position to see just how cosmically provincial such a viewpoint would be.*

There are indications that science is more amenable to the idea of the existence of God today than it was in the past. Clearly, the march of science does not supersede the need of man to believe in a supreme being—not, at least, for many of the scientists who are leading the march.

Duchesne　　*The scientist is much less ready to say today than he was before that God doesn't exist. He has absolutely no argument for such an idea.*

The connection between science and religion has perhaps never been so easy in certain respects as it is now. The scientist's universe has become so large, so wonderful, so unexpected, he almost needs God in some form, some fundamental principle.

Born　　*Those who say that the study of science makes a man an atheist must be rather silly people.*

With a scientist, then, as with every man, the existence of God rests on faith—unprovable, intuitive faith.

Some see no need for the God-hypothesis. Others are unconvinced. Many accept and nurture the conviction that God exists. Disagreement, yes, but universal emphasis on the right and even the necessity of the individual scientist to harbor his own view concerning the existence of God—a view that can never really be labeled either "scientific" or "unscientific."

I have profound respect for the universe. It is a most interesting and complex place. I do not look upon it as an accident. But this is not speaking as a scientist, because the point of whether it is an accident or not does not come out of the playing field of science. It's a no-no question. **Hynek**

We don't know whether evolution is planned by some kind of power or whether it is accidental. I do not believe in a creation by a higher form of life. Nobody knows. When someone insists that it is so, it is just as wrong as if he says creation is ruled out. It is a question of faith. **Wolf-Heidegger**

Science makes one aware that all answers are not available. Therefore, you have to call on an unknown and have faith in this being for the answers. Faith is believing without proof. I have never heard of anyone proving that there is a God. The fact that most religions are based on a God means that most people have some sort of faith. **Davis**

If we could define God mathematically, it would be a simple thing. But we can't do that. Faith goes beyond knowledge. Many people acknowledge only that which they can grasp and see. On the other hand, they would not argue that the universe doesn't continue beyond the Milky Way, even though they can't see it. But they believe it. You can't see God either. You can feel him. You feel that man is something very small and that there exists something very large. But I wouldn't argue about it. I haven't seen it. **Ehrenberger**
I don't think that a true scientist can, in the final analysis, be an atheist. It depends on whether a man

is tuned to this frequency or not. One can receive signals from outer space only if one is tuned to the right frequency. Much depends on whether man wants to find God or not. A certain subordination is involved.

Gjøtterud *If I believe already, it's easy for me to see the finger of God in nature. But if I do not believe, it's not necessary to see it. It is very important to remember that God has given man freedom. If he had made science so as to force people to believe in him, they would not have freedom.*

Turner *If you believe, no proof is necessary. If you don't believe, no proof is possible. I don't understand faith. To me faith seems to be the blind acceptance of something without proof. Whatever a man wants to believe, let it be for him, so long as it satisfies him and doesn't injure others.*

Alyea *Intuition is the essence of proof about anything spiritual. When a person has an intuitive feeling, and another person has it, and another, and another, someone who has no intuitive feeling in this matter may begin to feel that if all these other people have this feeling there must be some basis for its existence. In a sense, it's like the radio waves that are at this very moment passing through our bodies. We do not realize the waves are there unless we have a little instrument on which we can turn a dial and pick them up and translate them into music or words. So if you see people twisting these instruments and coming up with music, even if you don't have one of those instruments, you will begin to believe there must be those waves coming through, because these other people have experienced them. When enough human beings have had this experience and belief, then this is a sort of justification for your feeling. The fact that they have it shows that there must be* *something there. The fact that you have not experienced it means that you have not yet been tuned in.*

Science cannot find God, but the scientist can. **Autrum**

Do Scientists Need a God?

To say that the universe suggests the existence of God is one thing. To espouse a God with specific attributes and powers is quite another. Such espousals spring from faith, not from science. As may be expected, therefore, the God of the scientist is as individualized as the man who believes in him—or who decides not to believe.

A friend of mine asked an old priest in Korea **Rydberg**
about his religion. He said that he was not old enough to have a religion. Perhaps it's the same with me. I do not believe in God. I do not need a God. I can understand that some people do it and that they need it. It can be a great help to them. I have no use for a religion. I can't see what it should do to me. Of course, it would sometimes make things easier. If your children are sick at home, it's very easy to ask God to take care of it and then you can go to bed and sleep nicely. This I can't do. I have, of course, a moral of my own kind. It's rather similar to the Ten Commandments. I could make some small adjustments to fit my religion, but I haven't tried that. For example, "You should respect your father and mother." I think you should respect anyone. It's too limited for an atheist.

I don't know if I have ever believed in God. I was confirmed in the church. At that age I was not a strong believer nor a strong disbeliever. Since then I have become a very strong disbeliever. Any man may have his own beliefs. This is up to him. I don't heckle anyone who believes in God.

Newton tried to prove the existence of God. **Westphal**
Science has given this up. If there is a God, then I

67

am very sorry to say that he has never revealed himself to me. He could have done this, in fact he should have. But he didn't. Therefore I became an atheist.

Komar *I never use the word "God." I find the man in the street's usage of the word painfully naive. Although I cannot prove that such a thing does not exist, I'm quite sure that it doesn't. I would classify this as atheism. I do not believe that there is an independent volition to whom I can appeal to modify his decisions as to the way the universe is run.*

There is here no specific indication that science and atheism have a cause-and-effect relationship. There is, in fact, no reference to science at all.

Others prefer to leave their personal portrayals of God open-ended:

Forssmann *When I was a child, I pictured God sitting on the clouds and thought of him as a good old man with a long, white beard who rules the world and hears each individual. When I sit in an airplane and fly at a high altitude, then this whole world picture changes decidedly for me. The picture we have made of God is an interpretation of the Bible, which is a book of the time in which it was written. For example, I do not accept the idea that God took his pen and wrote the Bible himself.*

The explanation of God from the Bible alone is not possible. God is infinite, and as we advance in science he will remain infinitely beyond us and beyond our description. I cannot see God the way the theologian requires, but I am not justified thereby to deny his existence, which is revealed by his laws.

Pihl *I don't have a conception of an individual God, not a God who can influence the development in our world directly. I am always wondering very* *much about the very fact that we live in a world which is ruled by so few laws. The existence of such laws moves me, but that's all. I agree with Einstein, who explained it much better. This is a* mysterium *to me. But I have no need to explain this* mysterium *through an individual called God. It may be or it may not be. I just don't know.*

With regard to a personal God who functions in daily life, I have changed my opinion several times in the course of my life. I believe in a universal power, call it "God" if you will, since there is something beyond our knowledge. But whether this universal power can concern itself with the individual, as certain church dogmas have it, that a person can count on a better life here or in the hereafter when he does this or that or pays a specific tax, this I consider as complete nonsense. But there are cases in life where one asks whether it is coincidence or predetermination or what. Then one begins to waver. In spite of my age, I cannot express myself clearly. I am not certain.

Wolf-Heidegger

I am relatively hostile to the church, but by no means atheistic. I believe that a power, call it "God," assigns a task to man. Man is to perform this task freely and not as a serf who is under constant surveillance and who will be rewarded if he does his task well and be punished if he doesn't do it well. There are too many unpunished crimes in the world, both small and great, and too many people who are in misery. Such an interpretation is too simplistic. It is not that I wouldn't trust this central power, if it has really created the world, but I don't believe that it is concerned with the fate of the individual and with every sparrow that falls from the sky. I believe that it is one of the few tasks that distinguishes man from the animals that he must personally see to it that ethics are transmitted and to live by them, without expectation of reward or fear of punishment. It is simply his assignment.

Lombard   *My pastor tries to explain the notion of God with words that everybody can understand. His latest idea is that God is energy. That's a good idea. But it's more than that for me. It's not sufficient.*

If the search for the laws of nature suggests to some the existence of God, it may be because to them God and the laws are synonymous. Those who see it this way are obviously calling on their scientific background in looking for a personal definition of God.

Tangen   *For me the laws of nature and God are the same thing.*

Trümpy   *God is the governing idea behind the universe, something which makes sense. It means there is a governing principle which is ruling the world and giving some statistical sense to the evolution of the universe and humanity and to the personal set of rules as well, but not to the meaning of personal life or survival after death.*

Piccard   *If God gave man his brain, he would also know what man would do with it. Thus he gave part of his power to man.*

Nothing has yet been said of a God who really does anything as an individual (unless one thinks of nature's laws and man's intellect as acts of God). Did, for example, a personal God create the universe? What, indeed, does "create" mean? Or aren't these the right kinds of questions at all?

Hansen   *This is where confusion comes about, when one intellectually looks at a concept of God and asks whether he created the universe. I'm not impressed by that kind of a question. It's not important to me.*

I would think of God as the originator of the   "Oxford"
whole universe rather than someone who is directly
concerned with human affairs.

Perhaps it is more meaningful to speak of a God who is within every man; one who is really the answer to a human need. Rightly understood, such a God is important to well-being and daily living.

It's very hard for most individuals to think ab-   **Komar**
stractly. They've got to have something concrete to
picture. It's sort of a concretization of the abstract
concept of the ideal. To my mind, this is where the
concept of God comes from. I'm not opposed to
this concept. In fact, I approve highly of it. I just
think that one should recognize where it comes
from and what its abstract qualities are and get rid
of the irrelevant peripheral qualities. For example,
when something is made concretely an attribute of
an individual, then you think you can appeal to this
individual to get him to change his mind, which is
childish and naive. It's just the degree to which you
want to make your ethics concrete, the degree to
which you want to attribute it to something outside
of yourself. In a sense, it's diminishing yourself,
because if this ethical concept is really within you
and you realize it, then you have a better realization
of your own worth. To attribute it to something
exterior to yourself, saying that it's God and his
ideals, and unfortunately I can't measure up to it, is
sort of belittling yourself. It isn't God and his ideals,
it's you and your ideals.

When I try to understand where the concept of
God comes from in most individuals, I think they
have in their developed superego the concept of
what is the ideal to which they are taught to strive
or to admire, and they simply have the tendency to
personify or anthropomorphize this concept. In
other words, instead of recognizing it as an abstract

*ideal which they've been conditioned into learning
or approving of, predominantly through their community and family, they attribute this ideal to an
individual exterior to themselves which then is col-
lectively named God. God, to each man, is this ideal
toward which he strives, and where he got this ideal
from can be a subject of scientific investigation of a
rather crude sort, because I wouldn't approve of
taking babies and tampering with them.*

Whether the concept of God is exterior to man or
within him, a scientist sometimes feels that he is in part-
nership with something noble and transcendent—a partner-
ship that bodes well for life on our planet.

Inglis   *There are religions that use an anthropomorphic
God who is thought to have a very personal and
direct and human-like interest in each individual of a
sort that gives downtrodden and suffering individuals a relief from their suffering, a feeling of there
being some point to it even though their lot is so
miserable that life doesn't seem to be worth living.
Even a large number of people in our affluent society still feel an emptiness in their lives that is filled
by some such feeling about God.*

*Scientists tend to get away from this concept of
the creator, of something to fall back on personally.
In its place is a feeling of being in league with and
participating in the intentions of the creator to
amplify the well-being of life and living things and
trying to bring about some* summum bonum. *One gets
a feeling that in trying to advance science perhaps
we're partners in some greater enterprise. It makes
life additionally worth living to feel that there is
something beyond us that we're participating in.
The wondrous works of creation need to be revealed
to mankind for his good and that's what science is
about. We're not making the laws of nature, we're
revealing them and discovering them for mankind. If*

our feeling is that there is something great beyond us, but we're doing all we can about it, we don't call it religion, but it has analogies with what a monk will do in promulgating the word of Christ.

But what about a God who responds directly to human praise or supplication? Can science determine whether prayers are answered or not? What would the data show?

The quantitative aspects of science appear to be **Turner** *something that the religious faction devises all sorts of ways of circumventing. Take prayer, for example. I suspect that if one were to analyze the frequency of answered prayers the results would form some sort of random pattern, unless the act of praying should stimulate the one who prays to do something about it himself. One of my friends who is not a scientist and is quite devout has a simple explanation for this. He told me that his God is a real personal being and listens to his prayers. Such prayers may be answered if God sees fit and, if not, it is just simply God's will and it is God's job to know what is best. From the scientific point of view this is like throwing out negative data. I once had to reject a Ph.D. thesis because the candidate who was trying to relate the fluctuations of the Gulf Stream through the Florida Straits with the incidence of icebergs on the Grand Banks failed to include all the years when there was no positive correlation.*

Perhaps there is another kind of data, however:

I would shy away from the strictly anthropomor- **Hansen** *phic approach to God. It is far more deep and complex than that. One cannot ignore, for example, what might be deemed a truly religious experience. I think these experiences indicate that there is a force (and this is, at best, a crude use of the word) that exists in the universe that seems to work through*

73

man and to employ man as a channel for love. In the words of Rabbi Heschel, "God seems to be in search of man." When man responds to this search, his life is changed. It is as if some force or power flows through his life and reaches out to touch the lives of others around him. This would seem to me to be the prime message of Christianity. If one looks with care at the lives of the great religious leaders, such as Jesus Christ, one recognizes this tremendous urging to touch the lives of human beings of all classes and ranks. Certainly this is where the significance of the concept of "God in man" has its deepest meaning for me. But this concept of God is really the result of an experience. I, for one, cannot approach God through the media of rational thought. To define God, to explain God in rational terms, to me destroys the very concept of the feeling of a divine power that one has in a religious experience. The very concept of love itself is not definable in concrete and rational terms or verified by qualifiable methods. In short, love, like God, is experienced and not defined.

This brings one to such interesting questions as the use of prayer in relationship to a concept of God. The primary effect of prayer, from a personal point of view, is to open those doors and unlock those barriers that prevent the forces of love from passing through man towards his fellowman. Prayer also provides for a person a source of inner strength in that he articulates his greatest desires and needs and, in the process of doing that, comprehends his problems and perhaps their ultimate solutions. I would differentiate prayer in this sense from prayer in which one wants to effect changes in physical phenomena or cause occurrences to take place that might best be described as supernatural.

My concept of God does not include a concept where God is cajoled or perhaps talked into doing *that which we wish to have occur. In the process of prayer, anthropomorphic terms such as "Father" and "Lord" are used, and I would find no quarrel with this. One speaks and acts as if the God being referred to was in the image of man. These are symbolic terms and certainly have meaning in their own right, but to confuse these terms with the more profound concepts of God is to say that a switch which is thrown represents light. It merely represents a device which closes a channel through which energy ultimately flows to give light. Thus the use of familiar, man-like terms in describing God is a way of closing the switch to release the powers that apparently exist in the universe and that reach through and beyond mankind. With this concept of God, questions such as whether or not God created the universe and, if so, when and why, have little meaning to me as such. This is where one leaves the realm of rationality and truly enters into an area where man's mind has no comprehension of the terms being employed. I keep returning to the point that God is something that is experienced rather than that which is put as a cause for observable phenomena.*

Could it be, once again, that the act of sampling affects the outcome, that an objective opinion on prayer is not even possible?

I believe that God is the creator of the universe and the guiding force in the maintenance of the universe and of all things in it. He is more than the prime cause. He can answer prayer. These things cannot be dealt with statistically. **Friedrich**

My own definition of God is not based on any scientific observation. I can say, "I believe in God the Father, creator of heaven and earth," without any difficulty, if I say what creation means for me. I **Van Iersel**

75

believe in a God who has to do with the world. In my opinion, creation is much more than that in the beginning there was a God and then the business started, with its own laws. Creation is not bound to time. It is always there. In human terms, God is still concerned. When I say that God is concerned, this is something a religious man can understand and yet cannot understand. It is not just a projection, it is true.

Worcester   *Applied to prayer, the scientific method breaks down in every case that I know of. We've all heard of individual stories where prayer resulted in some spectacular result. I would like to feel that I have a certain amount of evidence that prayer has been useful, that there has been a response. But to prove it scientifically would be out of the question. The response might have been the same anyway. And you can never go back and relive it to see what would have happened in the absence of prayers. There are blanks that have to be filled in by faith that can never be proved scientifically, at least not on the basis of what we know now.*

Is even the question out of place?

Anderson   *Wanting intervention by God is the height of egotism. What makes it so important that, if God does exist, he should intervene, particularly for minor affairs like a little war or some personal circumstances?*

Understandably, personal definitions of God and his work often reflect the religious background of the individual. Those in whom faith in a personal God has persisted and grown speak of it with fervor.

Bjercke   *I believe in God, I believe in Jesus, and I believe in the Bible. I do not find that modern science has disproved very much of the Bible. Of course, I'm* *quite sure that the world is more than four thousand years old, but the fundamental truths of the BIble are not killed by modern science.*

I think of God in the Trinity, as a spirit, and yet as a man. I personify him in the Christian sense of Jesus Christ. God is the all-encompassing power that is personified in Jesus Christ. He has always been active and will always be active in response to human needs and to prayer and gives a certain satisfaction in the time of trial. **Davis**

It is difficult to define God. If one believes in God, one must find a form in which to serve him. My form is the one found in the Catholic Church, but I leave it open that other religious sects may also find God. The ways to God can come from different directions. **Ehrenberger**

4

Speaking of Miracles

However carefully men draw the line between science and religion, between the study of the physical universe and the concern for the spirit, there are always phenomena that defy delineation. An "incurably" sick man recovers. An event "forbidden" by the laws of nature is reported. Messages seem to be transmitted without the benefit of known means of communication. Someone accurately predicts the future. Such events touch both realms.

God or no God, inexplicable experiences and occurrences cry out for answers. How can these things happen— if, in fact, they do happen? Why do they happen? Dedicated to open-mindedness, the scientist should be able to speak to these questions.

What Is a Miracle?

A definition of terms is always essential to the scientist. Within the framework of the laws which are his domain, he is able to define a miracle by contrast:

Friedrich   *A miracle is something which happens which is contrary to the laws of nature. When you escape a seemingly certain collision on the highway, some people will call this a miracle. But this is not contrary to any natural law. It's something that just* *happened. Whether it was divine providence or not you can't say. It may be just a coincidence. But if you're speaking of miracles as we read about them in the Bible, where water is turned into wine with no other means such as sugar or fermentable material, this is contrary to the laws of nature and would be a miracle by my definition.*

Applying this definition in its strictest sense, some see no evidence of such miracles:

Scientists generally don't believe in miracles. **Alberty**
They don't become scientists if they're that type. You can't really be a scientist without believing that the universe is very dependable. If God were playing games with the scientist, and he couldn't depend upon things behaving the same today and tomorrow, he couldn't really be a scientist. His whole life is built on that kind of confidence that things are maybe mysterious but still consistent and well behaved. You don't have to invoke things mysterious. If you can't understand something or can't predict what will happen, or you can't get the same thing to happen again, it's your fault, it's not somebody else's fault. It's your lack of understanding. That is so key to a scientist that most scientists are pretty quick to reject things that don't fit in with that kind of a picture of the world.

I know of no evidence for any miracles. What I **Komar**
understand by miracles is something that happens in violation of the usual laws of nature. What is quite conspicuous is that the time of miracles was in the age of ignorance and the lack of science. Why isn't there a density of miracles today proportional to the density of miracles reported thousands of years ago? Quite clearly because people are more critical today. My favorite comment is the one attributed to Anatole France when he visited the shrine at

79

Lourdes and saw all the crutches there. He said he was very impressed with all the crutches, but what impressed him even more was that he never saw a wooden leg. If God can do miracles, why can't he make a new leg? It's rather interesting that those kinds of miracles don't occur.

Born *Something which is against natural laws seems to me rather out of the question because it would be a depressive idea about God. It would make God smaller than he must be assumed. When he stated that these laws hold, then they hold, and he wouldn't make exceptions. This is too human an idea. Humans do such things, but not God.*

"Oxford" *If some supercivilization can perform miracles because they have knowledge that we have not got, then there is something wrong with our science. It is my belief that miracles did not happen, but I am not willing to be dogmatic about it.*

But what about these laws of nature that are used to gauge the miraculousness of an event? In calling upon them so confidently, are we not overlooking the fact that the very existence of reliable laws is already a miracle of the highest order?

Tangen *Every small bit of science is a miracle. The greatest miracle is the existence of the laws of nature.*

Trümpy *It is a kind of miracle that man has managed to appear on earth, but a miracle which is certainly repeated in a different way on a lot of other planets.*

Ehrenberger *All of life is a miracle. When you look at an apple seed, you are really looking at a miniature fruit tree. This is as big a miracle as the news of the Resurrection. For me there is no such thing as chance. That an apple seed becomes an apple tree and not a chestnut tree is not a matter of chance. We have no* *influence over the process by which a grapevine grows. It is simply so. To me it is as much a miracle as the healing of a man at Lourdes. The two are on the same level.*

When I perform surgery and sew the wound back together and it heals, then that is a miracle for me. I have done nothing but open the wound. The miracle is that there are laws that govern the reuniting of the wound. For me, there is one miracle, namely that God has created the earth, that he has given it its laws and now lets it follow such laws and does not capriciously interfere. God knows no capriciousness. Primitive theology and God-representation always require that God break through natural laws in order to prove himself to man. The big miracle is that the spiritual support of the world is unchanging and unchangeable, and will not be changed capriciously. **Forssmann**

It would have been possible for the God that I visualize to create Christ as a full-grown individual, ready to go to work. He didn't choose this course because it wasn't required that he choose it. The plan that he used was a much simpler one. God set up the laws and then let things go. Man works with the laws and according to them. If he doesn't, he faces rather serious consequences. **Worcester**

The very power of healing is a miracle, but it does not have to be associated with God or theology. **Wolf-Heidegger**

What does a scientist do, however, with the report of an event that is clearly not explainable by any known laws of nature? It is not enough for him to say that he does or does not believe that such a thing can occur. It has been reported as a fact. It is in violation of natural law. What is the proper scientific attitude in such a case?

First of all, it is important for a scientist not to discredit unusual data out of hand.

Worcester   *It may very well be that there are perfectly well-documented cases where real, physical things happen that are unexplainable in terms of ordinary, readily known theories.*

Anderson   *If a very sound person had examined all the evidence and had concluded that he really couldn't find a sound basis for explaining an event, I wouldn't conclude that he had been a sloppy investigator. I would conclude that perhaps there isn't a sound basis of cause-and-effect relationship.*

Gjøtterud   *I would be very careful about disbelieving the witnesses of miracles, because then I have to conclude that they are lying. I would stay away from any explanation. Just accept it as a witness. I think this is the attitude of science, to be open-minded and not to close the world down and say things are impossible. I think it is an anti-scientific attitude to conclude that things are impossible.*

The element of uniqueness in miracles is probably the heart of the matter. If something happens only once, the scientific method cannot be applied to it, and a scientist will hesitate to discuss it from a purely physical point of view.

Hynek   *Science is powerless to deal with something that isn't repetitive. Galileo would never have gotten the laws of motion if he had rolled a ball down an inclined plane just once. He had to repeat and repeat and make many, many measures. Miracles are not in the field of the potentially, publicly knowable. There is no way of testing whether they did or did not occur. The scientist simply says, "It is not in my playing field."*

Autrum   *The miracles of the Bible are either miracles, in which case they do not interest me as a scientist because they are unique, or they are reproducible, and then they are not miracles.*

82

Our physical experience is seeing one side of the **Alyea**
shield and the spiritual experience is seeing the other
side of it. You can't use the same machinery to
measure both sides simultaneously. God is the one
who can see both sides at once.

Miracles are outside the field of science. You **Inglis**
can't repeat the experiment to find out if it really
works that way.

Miracles can only be discussed on the religious **Jeuken**
level.

A miracle is something that contradicts reason **Westphal**
and exact experience. My definition of experience is
something that is repeatable, an explanation of a
circumstance that everyone can check out with the
same results. We can only talk about something as
existing or having the possibility of existing if we
can prove its existence or have plausible grounds
that its existence can be proved.

Miracles are very special phenomena that just **Gjøtterud**
happen once. They are very difficult to tackle in
exact science because we don't have the possibility
of repeating the experiment. It's against the attitude
of science to deny this.

Most of those things which those who believe in **Horn**
miracles say are miracles cannot be researched. A
great geneticist has said, "Science can't use research
time for such work."

Strictly speaking, a unique phenomenon is not a **Van Iersel**
matter for science, because science depends on regu-
larity. So if a miracle could be reproduced a hun-
dred times, it would become a scientific matter.
Then it would be possible to give a scientific expla-
nation.

Or do miracles repeat themselves—and cease to be miracles—in the course of time? Scientific data are purely statistical, and so are the laws based on them. Science is young and data are never complete. Perhaps the laws of nature and the miraculous exceptions are all part of a larger, statistical whole. Is it all a question of probability?

Winand   *You may calculate the probability that a brick will not fall, but rise, and that would be a miracle, because the probability is so low.*

Brooks   *It's very hard for science to deal with reports of events that are long past. Science can really only make statistical statements about anything. Science can say that miracles, as described in the Bible, are highly improbable. It can never really assert that they never happened.*

Trümpy   *If you take a sufficient length of time, highly improbable events become probable. In evolution, mutations which give a completely new kind of animal and which can survive are extremely improbable. But taking into account the billion years which we suppose for the evolution of life, even such improbable events become probable.*

Waldman   *I have never seen a miracle. I personally have never been convinced of a miracle. But I am not going to say it's impossible. One of the most interesting things about science is that nothing is impossible. What happens is that things are more or less improbable. Consequently, you cannot make a positive statement that something is impossible. You can say it's highly improbable that something has happened. But then the people who are theologians will come back and say: Sure, they agree; miracles are rare. So there is no dissension.*

Piccard   *Miracles can be explained by probability.*

A miracle is a thing which has a very low prob- **Wallenfels**
ability, but it is not an impossibility. Most things
which are declared as miracles are not things which
are not possible, but things which have a very low
probability. If it is only by statistics that you make
predictions, there is a possibility that it will not
happen. You have a certain percentage of prob-
ability that another thing will happen, and of these
other things you have a small percentage of prob-
ability that a very good thing can happen, better
than you would expect. You could say this is a
miracle, or you could just calculate the probability.

A scientist can believe in miracles. But what do **Autrum**
you mean by a miracle? It is physically possible for
a stone to fall upward, according to statistical
theory. That would indeed be a statistical miracle. It
used to be said that masons waited for this miracle.

For different times you need different miracles. **Jeuken**
What is now no miracle at all may be a miracle for a
man who lived three hundred years ago.

As in all of science, the continuing examination of
evidence concerning miracles yields changing conclusions.

Poincaré said, "What is miraculous is that there **Duchesne**
are no miracles." I am not sure I would agree with
him. If Poincaré were still alive, he would perhaps
not make such a statement.

A main problem of each religion in the world is **Wallenfels**
how this world was created. Most people are inter-
ested in how the living part was created. Creation is
a very general expression and on the background of
the knowledge of each human being each one can
make a different creator. The more one knows
about how these things work, the more accurate
one's picture of the creator must be; and the lower
the knowledge is, the more general will be the type

85

of religion which one thinks is behind the organization. It is a question of definition.

Beadle   *Miracles are like unidentified flying objects. Science can't disprove either, but it can examine the evidence.*

So there is the very real possibility that what is now considered to be miraculous, and thus largely outside the pale of science, will someday be a legitimate and well-understood part of scientific knowledge. The events may still be the same, but the mystery will be gone.

Hynek   *In the history of science, things were called supernatural before they were called natural. Supernatural to me means something that we haven't learned about yet. What we call man's physical environment is perhaps not his total environment. I would like very much to come back in five thousand years and see what a textbook on astronomy or physics would be like. You may find that in five thousand years many of the things that theology speaks of will be found in our physics textbooks.*

Lombard   *Maybe in a few centuries we will deal with the notion of the soul in a scientific way. The notion of science will not be the same one we have, where we must have numbers and weight.*

Hansen   *By a miracle I would understand an event that has occurred, that has been observed, that defies commonly accepted beliefs about physical law and natural phenomena. As a scientifically oriented individual, I strongly cling to the concept of a rational structure of the universe. If an event occurs that cannot be explained by our concepts of the universe, I would record it as an interesting data point that perhaps can be explained as we come to know more. Insofar as miracles relate to physical events, I would wait for science to have an explanation at some future point in time.*

If a miracle happened, and I could not explain it **Alyea**
by natural laws, I would just say I don't know
enough laws. I would suspend judgment. I would
believe that it was still done by natural laws.

I wouldn't necessarily question the fact that **Mandel**
something has happened which is described as being
miraculous. I would question the explanation which
is given as falling beyond scientific investigation. I
don't doubt that healings may occur, such as those
at Lourdes, but I would rather look for medical
explanations than think of the intervention of a
nonscientific, extraneous principle to explain it.

What is now known is, after all, still only a small fraction
of what is potentially knowable. The scientist is in a
unique position to know and to emphasize this. The human brain has capabilities that are, at best, only partly
explored. No one can know the nature and extent of the
changes in our understanding of the universe that will
result when the human mind extends its outreach.

Only a small part of our brain is presently being **Piccard**
used. As we extend our senses, we must also change
our way of thinking.

I wouldn't discount the accounts of miracles. **Anderson**
There are a lot of things we don't know. We don't
understand all the ways in which human beings can
communicate with one another. It's not at all appar-
ent to me that everything that occurs is either
phony or can be readily explained with the knowl-
edge we have at hand.

There may be something which we can't detect **Mandel**
and which we can detect in the future and which
will play an important role in scientific thinking.
This will only complete what we know now. It will
not necessarily invalidate it.

87

Autrum   *A miracle can also be a subjective experience, but nevertheless real. A toothache is very real, even though the dentist doesn't find anything. Even so, a vision that I have can be very real for me. It can be a miracle for me and change my whole life. We know very little about the brain and central nervous system and what they depend on. In biology, it has been discovered in recent years that the geomagnetic field of the earth influences the behavior of people and animals. The daily cycle of man can be influenced by electromagnetic fields. Bees perform their dances differently when the electromagnetic field is changed. This has been known for only a few years.*

Worcester   *We tend to think in terms of transferring information by light waves or sound waves, but nobody has really been able to demonstrate whether there is some other kind of communication between people. I don't know whether one can isolate individuals in such ways that we could prove that we have some kind of electromagnetic connection that we're not aware of, yet I do know that sometimes there seem to be strange coincidences in the way that people arrive at conclusions or in the way that interactions take place. The investigation of these areas is not an encroachment on religion any more than the investigation of the laws of gravity was an encroachment on religion.*

Lombard   *There are natural phenomena which we cannot explain. A scientist has to observe such phenomena daily. For instance, we cannot accurately forecast the weather. We have to stop at a certain moment and say we don't know.*

Friedrich   *A person is what his mind is. What will happen when surgeons succeed in transplanting a brain? Is the person who receives it the same person? If there is a life hereafter, as I believe there is, will two bodies occupy the same space, or is the person who* *received the brain actually dead religiously? Has his brain been judged at the time he received another one? These questions have tremendous religious implications. Something that bothers me just as much is the use of chemicals to determine one's attitude. In religion, we equate hate with sin and love with purity. Now if I can take someone who hates and give him an injection and make him love, you can see the religious implications there. Does that mean that we can put sin in a syringe, or what? To me, these questions are much more serious and much more far-reaching than are the questions that have come up thus far.*

In showing a concern for the spiritual life of man, the preceding statement once again postulates an intervening God. One should, perhaps, let God be God.

I'm perfectly willing to grant God a tremendous   **Worcester**
amount of power and the ability to do anything he wants. We don't have to explain every last point in purely rational and physical terms. I'll grant God the ability to make changes in his plan here and there. After all, we see it in mutations of one kind or another, which do occur, and which are occasionally very constructive.

What we call a natural law is an abstraction. If   **Van Iersel**
one is really critical one can never say for all time to come that this law will be so. That is extrapolation. Let's view it in a historical way. The distinction was not rightly made to take God out of the world and make him just the primary cause, because in order to explain a miracle one has to introduce God again. I don't think this is a very fruitful way of thinking about the whole business. If I say that creation means always being busy, so to speak, with reality, then there is always the possibility of unique phenomena.

Worcester *I view God as a conservative type of being who would do everything in the most simple manner possible. If you have to have a miracle, all right, but if a small miracle will do, you don't bother with the big ones.*

Friedrich *With God nothing is impossible, and if he chose to perform a miracle contrary to the laws of nature, he would have the power to do it, since he is responsible for the laws.*

Duchesne *A man can believe in miracles and still be a good scientist.*

Are the Biblical Miracles Literally True?

Rarely are miracles described more forthrightly and explicitly than in the Bible, the world's best seller for centuries on end and the basic religious work of a major segment of Western civilization. The Old Testament is replete with the accounts of God's creative hand and of his miraculous preservation of his chosen people: the Noachian deluge, the parting of the Red Sea, the long day of Joshua, and Elisha's raising of the widow's son, to name but a few of the more dramatic incidents. In the New Testament, Christ is born of a virgin. He changes water into wine, he walks on water and through walls, he heals and vivifies. So do his disciples.

What do scientists make of these accounts? Some dismiss them summarily:

Westphal *I don't believe in miracles. They contradict our collective scientific experience.*

Born *The creation story in the Bible is not scientifically possible. Neither are many other things and all these miracles that appear there.*

Brooks *I don't believe in miracles. It is highly improbable that they occurred or that what was described was not, in fact, explainable by some kind of natural phenomena.*

Some see the Bible mainly as a product of its age. In order to evaluate the miracles properly, one must become familiar with the *Weltanschauung* of the men who wrote the Bible and those for whom it was written, and most especially with the state of what passed for science at that time.

If it's presented to us through the pen of a scribe of that time, then it's clad in the garments of that time.   **Bjercke**

We have accounts from a unique set of observers. My personal attitude is one of skepticism.   **Inglis**

The miracles of the Bible concerning the changing of materials must be understood as reports which were described by very simple people with the views of their time. If you read Mark Twain's Connecticut Yankee in King Arthur's Court *from this viewpoint, it is one of the most outstanding works of social criticism in existence. There are many valuable things in it, especially about miracles.*   **Forssmann**

I have to accept the Bible in the light of what was known by the people who wrote it, the society in which they lived. A literal interpretation is extremely difficult. If the people who were writing about natural phenomena had put them down in the light of what is now known scientifically, the words would have been a great deal different, and things would have been described in different ways. But I don't think this is necessarily in conflict with the acceptance of the broad picture and plan of creation and the plan involving the ultimate destiny of man.   **Worcester**

Besides, how accurate are the descriptions of the Biblical miracles or of other Biblical events? Is it possible for a book to be translated and transcribed over and over again and still retain detailed authenticity?

Piccard *The Bible is not verbally true everywhere. It has gone through many translations and interpretations. Mistakes may have appeared.*

Wallenfels *Of the reported miracles one has to be very careful. We know from experience how much things are transformed when reported from one person to another. A reported fact which comes to us over a long time through successive reporters could be a matter of bad information transfer rather than a miracle. In a chain of information transfer, there are always certain mistakes, just like in a book. You can't find a book without misprints. No newspaper is made without misprints. No translation or transcription of information is made without mistakes.*

Inglis *I look at miracles as folklore. Folklore builds up and grows in the process.*

Waldman *I have an open mind about miracles. I have questions about these things. I'm not completely convinced of them. What troubles me is that I've never been completely convinced, knowing the way I've seen things handed down and passed down just over my own lifetime by word of mouth. Watching the way science has been handed down and the maneuvers and things that went on in the past, I wonder how in so many thousand years you could really have accurate descriptions coming down. So I just simply wonder whether these things ever happened.*

Perhaps the whole matter of the credibility of the physical aspects of the Biblical miracles is only a minor point. The real importance of the accounts may lie in their purpose, no matter how large the credibility gap may seem to modern science.

I don't think of Christ as a magician, but as one   **Alyea**
who used magic to catch people's attention so that
he could convey more important ideas to them. A
scientist who is a teacher looks upon a miracle as a
means of establishing a bridge to a person he wants
to communicate with. If I really want to get my
students interested, I have to think of some gimmick
(an explosion, a cloud of colored smoke, a sudden
turning of water into ink); something with which to
get them aroused, something that's a miracle to
them. If I were Christ and I wanted to reach people,
I would reach them by doing something that to
them seems miraculous.

The term used in the Bible is "sign." It is not a   **Jeuken**
question of whether it can be explained by known
or unknown causes or not. Maybe it can be ex-
plained in natural terms. Anyhow, it is in the line of
nature. It talks about God. Also, what are the cir-
cumstances under which it was done? The striking
fact and all the circumstances together make the
miracle.

I don't literally believe everything recorded in the   **Bjercke**
Old Testament. This may be my scientific back-
ground cropping up. In the New Testament, people
saw things and wrote them down. This I put more
stock in than I do, let us say, in the books of Moses,
in which he tells about the creation, the flood, etc.
These stories have a purpose, and they are good, but
I don't believe in them literally.

An undue emphasis on the acceptance of the physical
aspects of the Bible's miracles may even be harmful to the
purpose of religion for modern man. Religion must be
much more than an awe produced by a seemingly supernatural event.

Miracles are not really necessary for religion.   **Trümpy**
They are very bad signs of religious fanaticism. The

three men in the burning furnace in the Old Testament said: "Know thou, King Nebuchadnezzar, that the God of Israel, our God, can very well bring us out of the fiery furnace, but if he doesn't take us out of the fiery furnace, this does not mean that we will reject the God of Israel and worship your God." This is one of the most wonderful answers in the whole Bible and it is a definite answer concerning miracles.

Lombard   *I wouldn't bother about such questions, because it is not the essential in the Christian message.*

There is a freedom, then, to view the purely physical aspects of the Bible's miracles as one wishes. It is possible to interpret many of them within the framework of the known laws of nature, and to do so does not necessarily deny the role of a God in the event or even make it less miraculous.

Alyea   *When you hear about the Red Sea engulfing Pharaoh and his men and saving Moses and the Israelites, some people go to such lengths to try to show how the wind piles up the sea at certain times and all of this kind of thing. I could believe that this could have happened, but I could also believe that if the Lord had wanted this to happen, then he could have made the wind pile up the sea and influenced Moses to go across at that time.*

Whether all of the miracles were true miracles or not I'm not sure. I could believe that they were. I could believe that anything is possible if the Lord wanted to do it. But he would probably do it using the physical laws. It doesn't make him the subject of any more adoration to think that he would snap his fingers to have things work than if he would work through natural laws.

Bjercke   *Since it's been proved beyond doubt that certain full eclipses have happened just about the time when* *the Bible describes them in its own words, I feel that then God was in on it.*

From a biological point of view, there is always a possibility of parthenogenesis. Nobody can say with one-hundred-percent certainty that it can't happen. **Van Iersel**

I would not find it impossible to accept the Virgin Birth. I would not call it a miracle. If I accepted it, I would say it is one of those extremely unlikely things which could happen once in every ten thousand million times. But that doesn't make it a miracle, just because it's extremely unlikely. **"Oxford"**

It was found recently that as many as one-third of the cells of the intestines are able to fertilize an egg. So it doesn't have to be a miracle to have a virgin birth. I'm quite willing to believe that this was done according to the laws of nature, but not according to laws of nature that have yet been discovered. **Alyea**

The change of water into wine may happen perhaps, or could have happened. Everybody was a bit drunk or happy and did not observe very well. The idea was transmitted that something that was above everybody had gone into this ceremony. I like this idea. It's exactly the same for the other miracles. **Lombard**

Perhaps the people were so thirsty that specially clear water seemed like wine to them. Also, wine in the Bible may not have been the same sort of thing that we mean by wine. I seem to recall that Joseph pressed grapes into Pharaoh's cup. This can taste very good, but it is not wine. I don't know what the people at Christ's time meant by wine. **Ziegler**

You can give a completely trivial solution to the miracle of turning water into wine. Through hypnosis you can make people believe they are drinking wine. They get just as drunk. **Tangen**

Piccard   *It is not unthinkable that Christ walked through a wall. The atom is mostly space. There is a probability that atoms can pass through each other without hitting.*

Rydberg   *Jesus was able to make people believe miracles through his unique and powerful personality. He had a very strong power over people.*

All this, however, may not be enough to make the Bible the power in people's lives that it has been over the centuries. A true leap of faith may be needed in the matter of miracles, just as it is in the matter of religion generally. Why exclude miracles from the leap?

Lombard   *The more you see of death the more it seems to be a very complicated phenomenon. So I wouldn't stop at the explanation given by people who have seen a very extraordinary life or end of a life of a man like Christ, with all his divine character. They have seen an abnormal case of death and they explain it like that. Why not? In a certain language, when our surgeons and medical men talk about death, they are talking about phenomena not very far from this one.*

Alyea   *I have faith that the resurrections in the Bible probably happened. Why did God have Christ come down on earth and suffer? Why didn't he just snap his fingers, if he was so all-powerful, and have the people learn things instantly? My answer is that he wanted to get us to understand how much he cared for us, and he could do this most lastingly and understandingly by having Christ as a* human *being, with the feelings of a* human *being. That was the only way that God could communicate to us, to go through the suffering of a father for his son. This was a* human *gesture, building a bridge from him to us in a way that we could understand. That's why I* *believe, as a Christian, that he did send his son, that he did come to save us.*

I accept the miracles. I believe that Jesus Christ   **Davis**
performed miracles. I believe he made the sick well and made the dead rise. I have no quarrel with this. I cannot explain it, but you cannot explain everything by science. If we try to, it's going to fall short somewhere. Since we don't know all the answers, I have to accept miracles as actualities, including our own resurrection and eternal life. Sometimes there is an element of doubt, but I have nothing else to fall back upon.

But should we really speak of miracles *in* the Bible, rather than viewing the whole Bible as a miracle? How else is one to account for its unusual reliability and permanence?

The Bible is a very wonderful document in many   **Inglis**
ways, and one of the most fascinating things is getting corroborations of some of the main historical events, like in the Dead Sea Scrolls.

The extraordinary permanence of the Bible   **Lombard**
through the centuries and languages and nations is a miracle.

What of the Ultimate Miracle?

Miracles or no miracles, it is possible to view the past, and even the present, with varying degrees of detachment. Moses' crossing of the Red Sea need not affect a man's daily activities or even the way he regards his place and purpose in the universe. There is a postulated miracle of the future, however, that is inescapably personal and urgent. It is the proposition of life after death.

Once again, the scientist will ask for a definition of terms:

Wallenfels   *Resurrection is a matter of definition. It is very difficult to define death. It is also difficult to define life. Most people define life as not dead, so you have to define death. It's easier to define death than life. Some years ago I gave a lecture on this subject to an audience of biologists. Some of them were zoologists, bacteriologists, botanists, and biochemists. If I have a preparation under the microscope and ask these people if it is dead or alive, I am very sure that each of them will give a different answer. For a bacteriologist, a dead cell is one which is no longer able to grow in a normal medium for this cell. For the zoologist, the main criterion is the reaction of the cell to certain stimuli. If he puts in certain chemicals and doesn't see any movement, he says it is dead. A botanist puts in a certain dyestuff. If certain structures absorb it, the cell is dead. If it doesn't, it lives. The biochemist will make an extract and see if certain zoological reactions are going on, if there are living enzymes in the cell. Each one has a different criterion for life. For each the definition of life is different. It depends on education.*

Anderson   *Man needs to feel that there is some way in which he can achieve immortality. This doesn't necessarily mean heaven or life after death. There are a lot of alternatives that are equally logical to me, and any one of them will do. But the one I like the best is that immortality comes in this world through being able to make sufficient impact on the world so that some part of the individual lives on. This impact can be through children, through ideas. For a scientist, the biggest part is ideas and it presents for him a very great source of being able to contribute. He contributes not only through understanding, but the new ideas he develops for that understanding make him live long after he's gone. So that's a kind of meshing together of science and immortality. The consequences of adopting this sort of view are a* *determination not to take a selfish view of life and of other people. If you're really going to continue to live through the people on whom you're going to have an impact, it makes it very important that you nurture your ideas yourself and that you have ways of convincing and persuading other people. You can't do that if you are a selfish individual.*

Is a distinction between the now and the hereafter even necessary—or desirable?

Salvation will only be understood by the religious people themselves. Salvation is already going on. I don't like to distinguish between this world and the next. In the Middle Ages, the church used the next world as a threat and as a consolation. I'm against that. Consolation is always necessary, but not in that way. **Van Iersel**

If a definition is that difficult, then it may be both archaic and unfruitful to approach the matter from a scientific point of view:

The afterlife does not have very much importance to me. I'm not interested in it. **Brooks**

In some ways, I'm not sure the resurrection is an important question. At least it isn't for me. I suppose that's one of the effects of being a scientist. In science, you very often find that there are many questions that you can ask, but some questions are very important and others are not. What separates good scientists from poor scientists is the quality of the questions they tend to concern themselves with. And I can imagine that the classic question of how many angels can stand on the head of a pin is an example of a question that is not interesting. I guess those questions are important for the church, but they are not important to me personally. **Alberty**

99

Hansen   *A man's whole outlook, his whole manner of living can be changed by religious experiences. I would classify this in the finest sense of the word as a miracle. One might extend this rational position to discussing concepts such as life after death.*

Life after death is beyond the realm of the comprehension of man. Whether or not the afterlife exists is somewhat comparable to asking the question, "Did God create the universe?" Explanations in either case are something that the finite man cannot grasp. The old, Judaic concept of life after death in a three-storied universe does not have much appeal to me personally. More than that I cannot say. I cannot comprehend, for example, the very feeling that there is that which is in the universe that seeks to love and that seeks to find the channel of its love in mankind. As long as I cannot comprehend that, I cannot comprehend what might exist beyond the mortal life of a human being. One might certainly hope that the capacity for love on the part of a man for those around him might, in some unknown sense, be preserved and perpetuated.

The youth of the twentieth century are not as apt to be swayed as the youth of other times by some of the classic concepts of theology and, in particular, by a concept that somehow the main goal of this life is to prepare one for a life of supreme joy in a heaven after death. The youth of our day are much more concerned with living a life that serves their fellowman and considering that to be a reward in itself. Yet there are those who find the more classic concepts of heaven and hell most meaningful and certainly a point for focusing their lives. I would not take issue with this except to say it is a different concept and a different approach. The trend of modern theology is perhaps away from these more classical ideas.

No one is saying that science can rule out the possibility

of an afterlife. It is simply not a scientific question—at least not for the time being.

I can believe in the Resurrection or not believe in it. It is not a scientific question. There is no scientific basis for it, not in the least. **Wolf-Heidegger**

Science cannot say anything about a resurrection. **Forssmann**

It cannot be ruled out with experimental science. **Davis**

In reports of miracles of resurrection, one has to be careful. You can extrapolate that in fifty years a doctor can take parts from fifty dead people and make a new organism, one living one from fifty dead ones. I don't think it is worthwhile to do this. **Wallenfels**

Every fact belongs to the field of science. However, scientists cannot be confronted with an infinite number of facts. They could not then arrive at satisfactory solutions. Because of the limitations of our minds, they have to make a choice. The choice is the most difficult step in the development of science, because you have to put your finger on the fact which has the best chance to be generalized. Facts which have been observed in very confusing conditions do not belong to that class. They are just exceptional facts. The tendency for scientists is not to look toward such phenomena. **Duchesne**

It's natural to worry and wonder about life after death. We exist on a time basis. We do everything by time. So when you think about eternity, it's impossible even for a scientist who is able to define infinity to conceive of what it is. You can look at it mathematically and use it, but the concept is still beyond our ability to comprehend, and this causes anxiety. **Friedrich**

I'm very much interested in some of the work that's been going on by highly respected people in **Hynek** *looking at evidences of reincarnation. I'm not moved at all by the fact that there are many more millions of people who believe in reincarnation than who don't. Nor am I impressed too much by the fact that, if I understand this correctly, reincarnation (that a person lives again in a physical body) missed by one vote being incorporated into the Christian doctrine in an early church council. I would never accept it from the standpoint that it's a nice thing to believe or explain this or that, but only if there were scientific evidence for it.*

Gjøtterud   *If you put a card in a box for each man who died and one in another box for each man who was resurrected, you would have one card in one box and millions and millions in the other. But I would not take the one card out. This is a question of honesty.*

Turning to nonscientific evidence, how much can we really say about life after death in understandable terms? How much help is the Bible in this respect? Is it even possible to explain something nonearthy to earthlings?

Trümpy   *The whole question of afterlife is very debatable, even from the biblical standpoint. You really have to scratch out the quotations which give much hope in that respect.*

Horn   *You will never find a man who says he believes in an afterlife and who does not put ideas in it from what we know here. All people who speak about an afterlife use knowledge from this concrete life and place it in the eternal, with no reason.*

Even an undefinable and nonverifiable concept can be important to man, however. Man may understand himself better by examining his own views. The process has therapeutic value.

I have no reason to deny such facts, but we do **Duchesne**
know the need of man to imagine as a real thing,
something that he loves. So it could possibly be that
the resurrection is simply the product of the imagi-
nation of man. This does not mean that we must not
pay much attention to such a process, because if
man has invented God, then where does this concept
come from?

A person can use such a belief in a resurrection **Wolf-Heidegger**
for soul support in order to get over specific diffi-
culties in life. He can say to himself that there will
come a time in the beyond when he can live without
these difficulties and pressures. It is a very typical
dogma.

It is interesting, and perhaps very significant, that even
among the most direct denials of a resurrection there are
the open-ended escape clauses that are so characteristic of
the scientist—hesitating to close the door, trying to find
other meanings.

It is very difficult for a scientist to believe in the **Horn**
Resurrection.

I can't find any good reasons for believing in life **Rydberg**
after death. I cannot believe that Jesus came back
from the dead.

I do not believe in a resurrection of the body. The **Forssmann**
spiritual emissions which man leaves behind him will
endure to a greater or lesser degree, but that we will
afterwards greet each other in white robes I don't
believe.

I cannot believe in the Resurrection of Christ, to **Westphal**
say nothing of the resurrection of Mary. I do not
believe in everlasting life, and I do not get excited
about it. When I am dead, I will know nothing any
more.

To believe something without tangible proof is never easy, especially not for a scientist. In spite of the difficulty involved, however, one of several reasons may compel him to accept a tenet that he can neither understand nor defend in a technical sense.

Bjercke *I have had a hard time believing in the divinity and Resurrection of Christ from time to time. Who hasn't? If it were easy to believe, then it wouldn't be a religion, would it?*

"Oxford" *The Resurrection has to be a miracle. I find it difficult to accept that, although I realize that as a Christian you've got to accept it.*

Van Iersel *The Resurrection is an important belief, not so much in order to make faith sure (because if you believe, then you believe in a resurrection), but because it has an important religious meaning. Christ was the first human to show that there is something else. You can see this only with religious eyes. I believe in an afterlife.*

Alyea *A logical person would say that immortality is sheer bunk. I will tell you why I believe in it. I once saw a man killed by a train. At that instant, from that moment on, I could not believe that the instant that his physical life was snuffed out, his spiritual life ended. From that moment on, I had no doubt about immortality anymore. I just can't believe that, at that instant, everything about that person stopped. This is not an argument. There is no logic about it, but it is a feeling that is so intense that I believe it to be true.*

Davis *We are not brought here on this earth to live and then die and that is it. So I think there is an afterlife. What it is like I do not know. I do not buy the concept of heaven and hell too much, especially* *of hell. We have all our hell right here on this earth. But there is something for us after this life. I cannot explain it, and neither can anyone else. No one knows.*

5

Learning from the Past

Who Won the Galileo Affair?

The idea that science and religion are in conflict has its origins in a number of historic confrontations between prominent men of science and the church authorities of their time. Of these incidents, the violent controversy involving Galileo is both typical and significant.

Galileo Galilei was born the year Michelangelo died (1564), and died the year Newton was born (1642). Thus he straddled the era between the end of the Renaissance and the birth of modern science. Indeed, the indefatigable Galileo had a large role in building the foundations of science as a discipline. His findings were prolific and prodigious, and any one of them was enough to make him world famous: the first astronomical telescope, the discovery of the craters on the moon and of sunspots and of satellites around Jupiter, the principle of inertia, the law of free-falling bodies, and more.

For more than thirty years of his life Galileo was embroiled in a running battle with the leading theologians of the day. The discord began when Galileo announced that his astronomical discoveries verified the Copernican theory of a heliocentric universe. The earth, he said, was indeed revolving around the sun, not—as the church and Aristotelian science had claimed for so many centuries—the sun around the earth.

The pressure against Galileo was relentless. Finally, at the age of sixty-seven, he was brought to trial and convicted of teaching Copernicanism. These were his words of recantation:

> *I, Galileo Galilei, now on my knees before your eminences, the cardinals of the Holy See, having before my eyes the Holy Bible, which I touch and kiss, do abjure, curse and detest the error and heresy of the movement of the earth.*

There is a legend, however, that as he rose to his feet he muttered, "But still it does move."

What is this incident saying to our time about the interplay of science and religion? Some have even gone so far as to propose a retrial for Galileo in order to focus attention on the importance of the issue and, if possible, to straighten records and reputations. Should this be done?

*The fight about Galileo is today complete non-**Born***
sense. Nobody should care about it.

But scientists are quick to see in the Galileo incident something that may be its most important aspect: that the conflict was not basically a religious one.

*The Galileo incident was a purely personal con-**Gjøtterud***
flict between two men.

*The case of Galileo had little to do with religion **Alyea***
per se.

*The conflict was between science and the church, **Autrum***
not between science and religion.

The church is, after all, composed of human beings with human shortcomings.

*The church erred in the past exactly the way we **Wolf-Heidegger***
humans err. It is important and even comforting to

107

realize that the church is human and not divine. It shows this again and again in its pronouncements. The point is that the church's taking of an attitude is exactly as fallible as that of a human being. If there is a God, then he is not fallible in his attitudes.

Komar *Religious leaders made fools of themselves in the past by going beyond their proper domain and asserting things which were patently wrong. They were just authoritarian priests, and I regard such religious leaders as having no more to do with religion than Stalin had. They were people wielding power over men's minds and physical power through force of arms. That's not really religion. It's a parody. Science has won a very important and major battle by crushing these people. I think they're so completely crushed that they hesitate to come into open conflict with science. At every turn they slink away. They know when they're beaten and they've been very properly beaten.*

Perhaps it was not even primarily a conflict with the church.

Autrum *The scientific advances of the Renaissance were not primarily a separation from the church. Leonardo was prohibited from dissecting corpses, not because it was prohibited by the church but because he was not a doctor. Science was freeing itself not from the church but from Scholasticism, and that is something else. The church was not connected with it.*

Whatever its role was, however, there is a widespread feeling that the church was stepping out of bounds into an area where it could not knowledgeably or effectively function. If this was done unwittingly, it can hardly be branded as a fault. But knowingly or not, the church was thereby weakening its position and influence.

The so-called conflict between science and theology came about because theologians speculated on matters that related to natural phenomena without employing the techniques of scientific investigation. It was not long before they ran into trouble with the scientists who were able to disprove the theories the theologians had set forth.

Hansen

In connection with Galileo, the church dealt with an area that was none of its business: the area of basic research, purely objective research.

Forssmann

The idea was very solidly entrenched in the Middle Ages that man should not seek to inquire into the secrets of God. Galileo and the scientific movement felt that this is no longer sacrilegious, but that it's man's right. God gave man a mind and he expected him to use it.

Hynek

It may be that the church deliberately overextended itself in order to stave off a very real threat to its power in medieval life and thought.

The church had certain beliefs which were based, perhaps, on the Bible, and certainly on interpretations of the Bible, and also on tradition. Either their education was poor so they couldn't see beyond this, or else, if they were the kind of people with active minds, they figured that threats to these beliefs were threats to the whole establishment. So they had to defend these beliefs. If the earth wasn't the center of the universe, then they couldn't have their religion. These ideas of the church were wrong. They forced religions and organizations to support things, in many cases, which scientists just couldn't accept and which wouldn't stand any kind of test of time. They could stop these things for a while, they could make Galileo recant, but it was all very temporary.

Alberty

Friedrich   *The confrontation between science and religious leaders at the time of Galileo was bound to happen, because up until that time people were relatively ignorant from a scientific standpoint, and the church felt that scientists and the scientific approach were dangerous to the power of the church. The church stepped out of bounds in trying to maintain its authority and concerned itself with things other than religion. The church tried to play scientist and did a very poor job of it. The fault was more with the church than with science.*

Davis   *The church was to blame in the case of Galileo. The church still has somewhat of a carryover in this direction. The church of several centuries ago was primarily a political structure. The practices of punishment and ostracism were political devices.*

"Oxford"   *The church has, in the past, always been very defensive. It has worried that the developments of science might take some of the faithful away.*

Such motives are ulterior, of course, and they effectively blind a protagonist to the real issues in a conflict. The church should have recognized that it was trying to champion an outmoded ideology, one that could be proven false by scientific investigation. Viewed in this context, the cause of the unhappy situation was simply ignorance.

Worcester   *The church was wrong at Galileo's time. It was too dogmatic and too literal and too unwilling to accept evidence that was extremely difficult to dispute. It was too unwilling to recognize that the God that they were talking about was perfectly capable of setting up the laws that Galileo was exploring. Churches can be terribly narrow-minded at times, and that was one of the times.*

Gjøtterud   *The church tried to harmonize its understanding of Christianity with the philosophy and knowledge* *of that time. It was not able to leave the questions open.*

The conflict was the fault of the church. The   **"Oxford"**
church didn't realize what science was all about.

This is not to say that science was entirely guiltless in the matter, however. Scientists are just as prone to human frailties as churchmen are. The scientific method was still in its infancy, and who was to set its boundaries?

The conflict was between science that was step-   **Autrum**
ping beyond its boundaries on the one side and religion that was doing likewise on the other side.

People were not aware of the assumptions from   **Van Iersel**
which they started, and they drew conclusions which were just too far from the starting point. It was not clear thinking.

There is, in fact, evidence to indicate that Galileo not only relished the conflict but did all he could to precipitate it. He knew he was right, and he was determined to crush his opponents. His intellectual arrogance matched the intransigence of the church. Both were guilty of intolerance.

Galileo was very arrogant, and so were the leaders   **Anderson**
of the church. It was a conflict between an arrogant man and, in the scientific sense, a group of anti-intellectuals who felt a threat. It's not the first time that the church has been dominated by anti-intel-lectuals. There was fault on both sides. If Galileo had been even a second-rate politician, he could have smoothed the whole thing over. On the other hand, it meant for him the compromising of scientific principles. Besides, he knew the church was wrong. From the point of view of the church, it meant compromising a deep religious principle which couldn't be compromised. That's the definition of a conflict which can't be resolved: when both sides

take the position that their positions are irreconcilable principles.

Waldman   *You run into conflicts of Galileo's sort in periods of time when there is very little tolerance. This can happen any time you have an intolerant form of government or an intolerant form of religion.*

Westphal   *Galileo was not to blame. Neither can I say that the church was at fault. It concerned the entire spiritual concept of the church of that time. The church was dogmatic and untractable about the position of the earth at the nucleus and center of the universe. Man was considered as the special creation of God and the highest attainment of his earth. The church's judgment was understandable, yet regrettable.*

Alyea   *Here were ecclesiastics, the big people in the community, and suddenly something new, the university, reared its ugly head. The human jealousy that is in all of us, whether we're religious or not religious, rose up, and the priests saw that something was threatening their authority in the community. That something was the men of learning. So this resulted in a battle, not between science and the church but between two groups of human beings who were jealous of each other. Out of this emerged the scientists who pooh-poohed the teachings of the church, thinking that this would strengthen their position, and the ecclesiastics who scorned the scientist because he was a man of no faith.*

What Is the Record of the Church?

Are we then to conclude that the historic clashes between science and the churches were largely the fruition of human failings, that the verdict must be couched in the relatively neutral tones of mutual intolerance? Is religion only minimally involved?

Scientists are reluctant to make sweeping statements of any kind, particularly in connection with fields other than their own. Yet they can point out instances and trends that may help to formulate answers.

Some of the data are negative for the churches.

Religion probably started out as an explanation of physical and biological phenomena for early man, and when it began to conflict with objective observational and quantitative analysis, the split began. Galileo and Darwin are probably the two best-known names associated with the upsetting of the theological applecart. There are others, such as Servetus and Harvey, who were also contributors. **Turner**

Where there was no knowledge existing which had been acquired by scientific methods, beliefs and faiths had grown up which had filled that vacuum. These were, by and large, associated with religion. Therefore, when science began to have something to say about these areas, there was bound to be a clash. **Brooks**

The Christian church had a great task in the early Middle Ages in keeping up the great centers of learning and science, but in the late Middle Ages the development of scientific thought was not produced by the church but largely against the church. **Trümpy**

I am convinced that if we hadn't had religion and the church and we had developed from the Sophists, we would have made progress much, much sooner. The first interest of the church has never been scientific research. **Horn**

But when all the information is in, it may not be possible to label the church as either a significant help or hindrance to science.

There were certainly times when charges of heresy by the church against those with other views **Ziegler** *interfered with the progress of science. I can imagine that someone who is well acquainted with the matter can cite hundreds of examples of how the church has hindered science, and I could not refute it. Similarly, someone could also say that, by and large, the church has helped science very much.*

Mandel *In many periods and in many circumstances, the church has not been favorable to the development of science. But I don't know whether we can say that if the church had not been present science would have developed much faster. It is a subject of speculation. It is like asking what France would be like today if Napoleon hadn't lost the Battle of Waterloo.*

This is only the human side of the question—the side on which people interact with people, scientists with churchmen. What can be said on the far more fundamental matter of the historic interplay between the experimental method and theological concepts—in other words, between science and religion?

The scientific method and a religious awakening sprang up simultaneously in Europe. Was it a coincidence?

Lønsjø *Some have said that it is no accident that science has flourished in the Christian countries, simply because the Christian's conception of God is something outside of nature and not some magical power of nature. A personal God created nature and left it for us to explore. Luther emphasized personal freedom, while the Catholics emphasized duty to the church. It would be strange if there weren't some connection with the progress of science.*

Inglis *There is a connection between the history of Christianity and the growth of modern science. Christianity gave birth to the scientific method with its emphasis on the value of the individual. It's not* *just a coincidence that modern science started in western Europe and not under Buddhism or Confucianism. The emphasis on the worth of the individual has been a great thing in Christianity, as contrasted with Oriental fatalism. Religious dogma has been of a nature, on the one hand, to subject the individual to church discipline but, on the other, to emphasize that each individual has a connection with God and the Savior in a way that gives the individual a special feeling of worth in his own mind. This is the seed of undoing of religious dogma. People felt their individual worth enough to respect their own ideas and rebel against the more repressive parts of the dogma. So we had the Reformation, which was the breeding ground of the most effective science that's going on in the world.*

There is undoubtedly a causal relationship between Christianity and the growth of modern science. It may be indirect, but it's important. The emphasis of Christianity on the worth of the individual had a large part in fostering the scientific revolution. In a certain sense, it was accidental that the church was the driving force in science in the medieval period. The church was the only repository of learning. Science in its modern form really arose outside the church, although it drew very heavily on the things that had been done before under the church. But science as a social system is strictly secular. The body of knowledge which is science certainly had a lot to do with the church, but science as an accumulative addition of knowledge is a distinctive and separate thing from the church.   **Brooks**

It would seem that this bodes well for the peaceful coexistence of the two camps as time goes on. How is it in our day?

Wherever the church has absolute state power, clashes with science will occur. But, thank God, the   **Wolf-Heidegger**

115

church no longer has this power to interfere and to give us another Galileo incident.

Forssmann *Now the churches all have cold feet and don't want to be included when it is said that they hindered the progress of science, and they do it wrong again.*

Van Iersel *There is a little bit of uncertainty in science today, but that is more of a shock to the religion of science than to the religion of a religious man. Science has a kind of religious notion.*

Friedrich *Religious people are very jealous of their beliefs. They want to be comfortable in their religion. They want to feel that they have the answers and don't have to fear the unknown. When anything comes up that tends to shake their beliefs, whether they are major or minor ones, anything that they've been taught in their religious lives, they tend to attack it, for fear that if they lose any part of their religious life they've cast a shadow on all of it. They can't stand to doubt and can't live with doubt or fear of something they've been taught to be false. So they lash out and attack it.*

So a plethora of conflicts remains. A broader look at the function of the church may even reveal that conflicts are part of its mission.

Brooks *The church can never completely avoid conflicts, because even value judgments have a predictive component to them. In many cases values turn out, on closer analysis, to be incompatible with each other. One set of values has consequences which degrade another set of values. When that happens, one has to make a choice as to which set of values one is going to adopt. This always hurts people.*

Nevertheless, common ground is being found in the concurrent advancement of religious and scientific thinking.

116

The time may come when the Christian church or some other church will bless the people or the instruments that fly to the moon and thereby legalize the entire teaching about space, which was previously considered heresy and an attack on the teaching of heaven and earth.

Wolf-Heidegger

In the nineteenth century, science and religion conflicted because scientists said that the future was predetermined. Then nuclear science found that the future was merely a probability. This opens the door to God again. So there should not be any conflict today.

Piccard

6

Learning from Youth

If, as Antonio says in Shakespeare's *Tempest*, "What's past is prologue," then surely the present is the harbinger of tomorrow. The continuing unrest on many of today's campuses brings this past-present-future linkage into sharp focus. Many scientists, especially those who are close to the classroom, are deeply concerned about the attitudes of youth and about the directions these attitudes provide for science, for education, and for man's understanding of his own and his neighbor's needs.

What Is the Measure of Interest?

Are today's college students concerned about religious questions? Do they attend church? How does their performance in this respect compare with that of a generation ago?

There is evidence that the interest is as lively as it has ever been:

Turner   *We used to discuss religion when we were under-graduates. In our bull sessions there were three things we talked about—money, sex, and religion—but I don't remember in which order.*

Hynek   *Students are not disenchanted with the questions that religion does or should deal with. I used to*

118

teach a course in which I would ask the students in the first hour, "What are the questions that interest you?" We would fill the blackboard with them. We found that eighty to ninety percent of these vital questions science couldn't touch, and rightfully so.

When you go to church today, you will find very many young people. The fable that people don't go to church today originates with those who have never seen a church except from the outside and who sleep on Sunday mornings.   **Ehrenberger**

Students are interested in these questions today. It's only a problem to discuss them with students. Students will not come to the professor themselves and ask him. A better thing is to make the education such that students will come and ask these questions.   **Wallenfels**

I'm very much pleased to see a great many college students in church just about every Sunday when school is in session. They have a genuine and healthy concern with religion. I think that, at some time or other, all students are concerned with religion. Many of them have exercised an independence, have broken away and are exploring all sorts of things, and within a few years will settle down and will have a feeling of need and will accept responsibility, and will become active in churches again.   **Worcester**

An astronomer very frequently gets religious questions from his students, because somehow they get the notion that an astronomer is perhaps a little closer to examining the heavens than other people are.   **Hynek**

Our students are concerned with religious problems. They do not go to church very much. It is not the age for it. But this generation will go to church just like their parents. They are not revolutionary in that sense in our country.   **Lombard**

119

Waldman   *Our student body is very predominantly Catholic. Most of them are quite active in church affairs.*

Alyea   *For twenty-eight years I used to have three groups of boys of about fifteen students each come over to my house for their class every Wednesday night. We'd have a roaring fire and doughnuts and apple cider afterwards. They'd have a weekly test when they first came in; then for a half hour we'd discuss lecture material and assigned material; and for another half hour we'd discuss an assigned book. And the ones you wouldn't expect to be religious would be the ones, perhaps, that were most devout. They would argue at length about this, very interestedly. It was wonderful to see a big, husky football player bending over a scrawny little fellow and shaking a finger at him and shouting, "I tell you, there is a God!" I hoped that some wealthy man would come forward and would give money for other young instructors across the country, so that they could be able to afford to entertain their weekly classes in their homes.*

Waldman   *The younger scientists are far more interested in religion from the standpoint of its being personal.*

These are evaluations of science students by science professors. This may be doubly significant in view of the fact that the typical science major has less free time for nonacademic pursuits, including religious activity, than do most other students on the campus.

Davis   *Students bring up religious questions in class, but scientific students are not as much involved in these questions as are the so-called liberal arts students. Students in science do not become involved in these questions until they come out and become older; then their thinking starts broadening and they often become very active in community affairs.*

Science is a master that demands a great deal of **Waldman**
you. Let's take a typical case of one of our students.
When we start with a graduate student who comes
here with a bachelor's degree, we expect him to put
in seven days a week, sixteen hours a day. And they
do it for five years. It takes total devotion. Sure he
can slip off and dash off to church, and he does
that. But he really can't play a big role in the
church. He can't be a leader ·in the youth move-
ments and things like that. There's just no time.

Interest, yes, but not necessarily a blanket stamp of
approval on either the religious past or present. Youth
wants to know. Before making commitments, it wants
answers. But who has the answers? Even schools of theology are stunned by the urgency of the search. It is a time
of confusion and of changing patterns.

The dean of theology doesn't know what to do. **Lombard**
They even have Communists as students in theology.
They have people who don't believe in God. They
are interested in the problem and attend the lectures
and try to get a degree.

Youth is very definitely leaving the church. **Friedrich**
They're confused. This is evident in the tremendous
increase in mental health deficiencies and problems.
Youth is disenchanted with the church, with people,
with themselves, with their peers, with society in
general. They've got the questions but nobody's got
the answers.

Our students are religious, but the general culture **Duchesne**
seems to me to be in retreat. Our generation has
entered an era where the practical problems have
become so important, where material evolution has
been so hurried, that the idea has developed that
classical culture doesn't mean very much and ought
to be eliminated, that religion is not important at
all, that God doesn't exist.

121

What Are Their Disenchantments?

It is typical of youth to strive for change. But what, specifically within the science-religion environment, are the reasons for dissatisfactions? As clearly as their teaching elders can determine, science-oriented youth appears to be unhappy with "organizationalized" churches and their formalisms.

Jeuken   *Attending church on Sunday is a kind of formalism. Young people are enemies of formalism. This does not say that they are irreligious or areligious. I think that young people are religious in their own way.*

Trümpy   *Most young people are completely disenchanted with the church, or they just take it as a place where you get married and nothing else. The church is part of the establishment.*

Hansen   *When we were younger, it was a very rare thing to hear a person say, "I don't believe in God." Now it is rather commonly heard. What many of our young people are saying when they use this phrase is that they don't believe in God in the sense that God has been defined rigorously and rationally by an institution such as the church.*

Wolf-Heidegger   *Whether the church is getting through to youth today is a very big question. In every land, East or West, the influence has become weak, and I think morality has certainly not improved. This could be the result of a greater enlightenment and rebellion on the part of the individual.*

Beadle   *Some students are disenchanted with the church. They ask, "What has the church done?" The church has tried. Its record doesn't seem better or worse than that of other institutions.*

The church has really failed youth. The church   **Friedrich**
*does not relate to youth and its problems. It talks in
generalities instead of dealing with specific problems
and specific answers. It talks in the language of the
Bible, and when kids try to get away from that and
ask other questions they're put off and not given the
answers. The church seems to be devoting itself to
the old people. It's a church for the dying and the
dead and not for the young and the living. Youth
opposes ritual and the liturgy of the church. Young
people don't go to their ministers with their problems because they think they're going to get a stock
answer regardless of the question.*

It depends a great deal on the age and experience   **Davis**
*of a person. At one time I fell out with the church
for reasons of the racial practices that were in vogue.
But as I grew older and went through the trials and
tribulations of just living every day, I felt that there
was a need that could not be satisfied except
through God. I think this is typical, not only of
scientists, but of all human beings. As people get
older, they have a tendency to feel a need of God
more than they do when they're younger. When
they're younger they get involved in other things
and they feel very self-sufficient, but as they become older they get less and less self-sufficient.*

The disenchantment also extends to parents, both for
what they are and for what they are not in a religious
sense. The past is replete with mistakes and the present
with sham, and youth is particularly quick to see these in
the family environment.

Youth is, to a certain extent, critical and wants to   **Ehrenberger**
*fight for freedom. Sometimes they miss the mark. If
youth is less religious, it is the fault of the parents.
You can't tell a child to go to church and not go
yourself. You have to live an example for them. If
you believe something you should also live it.*

123

Wolf-Heidegger   *A young man who is at all respectable will ask, "What has the older generation done?", referring to the horrors of the concentration camps, etc. The fact that youth searches for an answer, whether in the church or elsewhere, is a sign of the idealism of youth. Youth does not change. It tries to do its best. Whether it will depart from this course is another matter.*

Friedrich   *Youth is rebelling against the hypocrisy of adults. If parents weren't such hypocrites, the children would realize that the parents don't have the answers and, being really no different from their children, have to look for the answers in their religious lives.*

The disillusionment runs the whole gamut—from the church to the home to the laboratory. There is an impartial honesty in this, and a good share of the ironic. Should not science, with its relentless objectivity, be the ultimate bulwark against deceptive values? But perhaps its very lack of feeling has turned youth off.

Lønsjø   *It is only natural and right that young people are less enthusiastic about science than they were some years ago. They have discovered that it doesn't answer the deeper questions of life.*

Brooks   *There is a general falling away among young people from all forms of intellectual discipline. The more organized and hierarchical a subject is in its structure, the more the students revolt against it. Everybody wants to solve problems instantly, and science is too slow. There is a great sense of impatience. The attitude is that direct action is needed.*

Some of today's youth are disenchanted with science. This is based on the belief that science is not very relevant to the problems that immediately concern them, at least the physical and life sciences aren't. The physical sciences are under a special

124

cloud because so much of physical science is associated with war-making potential.

Inglis

Some of the best of our young people are the sensitive ones. They are disillusioned with national policy and its handling of the instruments that science has put in its hands. It's a revulsion against the whole system, which includes science but is not principally science.

Alberty

Young people are more socially aware today than I was as a student, and this tends to draw them into areas of the university that are more immediately concerned.

Beadle

Many concerns of young people are legitimate and well founded. As a result, interest of students in social sciences seems to have increased faster than has interest in science. Many students blame social problems on the misuse of science. Science per se is not good or evil, but its applications may, of course, be either.

Duchesne

The church has not been conscious early enough of the danger. Perhaps this is a consequence of science, the material development, and putting stress on the objective mind and rationality, frequently without very good consequences. Our students have felt the results of this, and they are interested in the horrible consequences of badly used science. Our youth has broken the bond with the real foundation of our civilization. That is perhaps one of the worst consequences of our civilization which has, in other ways, produced a society where everybody is well fed, buys everything, and gets anything. Our students are so well fed that they tend to deny the validity of this. This is the revolutionary movement of the students.

125

Are the Protests Religious?

When disenchantment turns to protest, it becomes difficult to ignore. As youth chooses this route, adults ask whether the movement is primarily a negative one or whether there is in it a recognizable plea for positive values that are minimized or even totally missing in our culture. If so, we should all be listening, and scientists and churchmen alike should be implementing the necessary changes.

Scientists see an emphasis on ethical values, rather than on religious tenets, in today's protests.

Komar   *Students are showing tremendous concern about ethical considerations and values and about the function of learning and knowledge in general. This has come up time and time again in their arguments for restructuring the universities, and I think they're absolutely right. Immediately after World War II, the values of students were to get ahead and make a buck in the world. Now the values have changed, for the most part. Students are more interested in their fellowman, and justifiably so.*

Trümpy   *The left-wing philosophy, mainly of Mark Hughes and quite a number of others, is taking the place of religion in the belief of students. Many students who have never read Mark Hughes or are unable to read him are running after these things, just as a lot of people go to church who have never even bothered to read the Bible seriously.*

Autrum   *As the population grows, the freedom of the individual becomes more limited. Then, as in the animal kingdom, migrations result. But where can one migrate today? So youth resorts to an inner migration, into the basements of Liverpool, etc., and says you can't tell them what to do.*

Hansen   *Look at the youth and student protestors in our schools. I see evidenced in their statements a fantas-*

tic concern for human welfare. On the other hand, in few of the demonstrations and overt statements does one see any reference whatsoever to religion or religious concepts. To a large extent, youths see themselves being lost as individuals. They see pressures around them hemming in their lives and finally say that they must relate to each other if their lives are going to have significance. Now this is not a religiously motivated response. It comes from a deep concern about a person's relationship to himself and to those around him. Religion certainly could play an important role at this point, but only if it transcends the traditional lines of the past.

If, as an astronomer, I want to interest students in astronomy, I would not start talking to them about the equations of celestial mechanics. I would find out what their particular connection is, what connects with astronomy in their daily experience. "Why does the sun rise later today than it did yesterday?" or something like that. If they are curious and have minds that are amenable to that sort of thing, they themselves will build the fire. Perhaps the analogy is valid and perhaps it isn't, but it seems to me that if I were intent on getting my particular religious views across to youth, I certainly could not talk to them in terms of theory, doctrine, or absolutes. But I would certainly hit them on the immediate issues of living, war and peace, ethics—lifemanship, essentially. Only much, much later would I talk about the theological aspects. **Hynek**

Students today are much more concerned with society than with religion. They're interested in religion only in terms of ethical values. Those who are not disenchanted with the church look at it as a vehicle of reform of society rather than as a form of personal reinforcement. **Brooks**

127

Trümpy   *There are few discussions on religion among university students. The political discussions are of much greater interest nowadays than the religious ones.*

Hansen   *What I sense is the feeling that the theology of early Christianity no longer has appeal to modern, twentieth-century youth in the way that it did to early Greeks and Romans who were conditioned along certain lines of thought by the culture of their day. This leads to concern on my part in that I am recognizing more and more that such anchor points as many of us had in the church and in patriotic attitudes toward the nation are no longer as evident in the youth of today.*

Friedrich   *Old people have obvious needs. They're approaching the end of their lives, and they're worried about it and about the hereafter. But you can't reach young people with that need. Death is the farthest thing from their minds. It's not a need for them. Their needs are the questions that confront them today: the upcoming test they can't pass, their future careers, sex, alcohol, race, etc. These are needs and youth needs answers. Is the church going to provide the answers or is it just going to talk over their heads? If it does the latter, it will not be a living force in the community.*

It is not a foregone conclusion, however, that the protestors are really the voice of youth in general.

Beadle   *There is no such thing as "they" with regard to the younger generation. Its members make up a broad spectrum of society. There is a small component of very vocal, disenchanted individuals who regard much of what is established at present as so wrong that they would destroy it and start over. Some have no conception of what they would build in its place.*

Only eight or ten of the eight hundred students in **Davis**
the Engineering School are really active in these
movements.

Yet, majority or not, youth is pointing to a "religion" that is much more personal than the dogma-oriented variety of their forebears. How can a belief be motivational if it is not freely chosen and individually forged? In this context, all agencies of learning, including science and the church, become resource centers from which to draw raw data for personal living.

I've discovered that religion is becoming more and **Waldman**
more a personal thing with students rather than an
organization or a show, wearing it on your shoulder
and marching down and doing things.
There has been clearly a falling off in attendance
at Mass at the university. I don't believe that this
represents any reduction in the religion of the
people. It represents essentially the concept that
there is a great deal of religion that should be
internal.

Students nowadays are not so interested in such **Pihl**
generally formulated religious problems. It may be a
danger. Now they have other problems which are
perhaps also of a religious nature, although not
religious in the specific definition of the Christian.

Children will go to church as long as the church is **Wallenfels**
able to answer questions in a way which they accept
as good answers. Of course, the general education of
the children will affect how long they accept the
answers as real answers to their questions. It is the
same thing in the education at home. In the house
of my parents, the answer which the father gave to a
question of a son or daughter concerning good and
bad was accepted much more than it is nowadays.
You can't tell your children today that something is
so just because you say it.

"Oxford"   *I would like my children to be brought up in a Christian environment, and indeed they are. Then, when they reach the age of eighteen or nineteen, when they can really think for themselves, they can decide for themselves whether they want to carry on being Christians or whether they want to give it up entirely and adopt some other religion. I think our children should be given a good grounding in Christianity so that they know what it's all about. If they accept it, fine—and if they reject it, they have good reasons.*

Rydberg   *Many young people are unhappy. Perhaps they don't want to believe in God, and one shouldn't force them to. One should help them to find other values in life.*

Davis   *The protest of young people is just another form of religion, a form to which we are not accustomed. I have been very much impressed with the students who have worked with the religious leaders or the civil rights movements and the social programs. They are expressing a kind of religion, or at least a set of tenets to live by. They have more concern for their fellowman, concern which they are actually demonstrating, than we had when we were young. I think they're sincere, and I think it is a religion. The churches should take advantage of it. The youngsters are doing what the churches have done for many, many years. The churches are really playing a game of catch-up. Fortunately, we have a group of young people going into the churches as priests and ministers who are inclined in this direction. They are being persecuted to a certain degree by the established church because it resists change. But I think these young people are right, and if the church is going to continue, it must change. The past practices could exist when people were not thinking. People think now, and they do not accept as readily as they* *previously did. So when churches come up with something, it's got to be good. They can't just sell anything to these youngsters. I think this is what these youngsters are really demonstrating.*

One can only hope that youth will retain its optimism for better living.

I see no reason for optimism in the next genera- **Davis** *tion. Although the youth are expressing themselves more today, I'm not sure their thinking is different basically from that of all the young people that went ahead of them. I am not sure that these same young people are not going to change and do just as we of the older generations have done. We become comfortable. We give up our ideals. We start thinking more about the facts of life. I'm afraid that the very same thing will happen to these young people who are so vocal today.*

But perhaps the difference between the "now" generation and the one that spawned it is big enough to prevent the evaporation of youth's dream. There has, after all, been a marked improvement in the transmission of information, and one of the results is a more widespread maturity and potential leadership in the young. In this lies a very real hope for the future—and a message for those who would influence its course.

One of the big differences between youth today **Worcester** *and youth in my generation is simply that the kids these days are much better informed. They know a lot more about what's wrong with the world and what's right with the world. They are more mature than we were.*

I'm more worried about the parents than about **Alyea** *the young people. I have tremendous faith in the young people. However, it is the impetuosity of the young that we must be careful of. They want mira-*

131

cles to happen overnight. I have no fear of the young people losing interest in religion, provided that religion is kept up to date and in tune with their feelings. Our young people are in a far better position to really understand religion than we were. We blindly followed. They are leaders. They are active in the church in their own particular way. They are much more leaders of Christianity than we *were.*

7

Of Churches and Churchmen

While it is possible to define science and to trace its development in a more or less systematic way, the same is not so easily done for organized religion. "The church"—which, in common parlance, is the all-inclusive term for faiths and denominations of every sort—is characterized by a history as checkered and strife-torn as many of its political and social counterparts, especially within the last four or five centuries. Even the language of religion tends to complicate the matter:

> *I've always wanted to know how the theologians* **Hynek**
> *think. When you go into a bookstore and ask for a*
> *textbook on physics, they will say essentially the*
> *same thing. But if you ask for a textbook in the-*
> *ology, you may be in some difficulties.*

Hence, when the scientist comments on the church—its failings and future—he is fully aware that generalizations, which are difficult enough to substantiate in his own field, are totally unwarranted in something as complex as man's organized religious activities. Yet, each man has the ability and the right to evaluate the effectiveness of churches in their roles as purveyors of religion, as he experiences it in his own life or sees it reflected in the lives of others. To the scientist, as a scientist, this becomes a matter not so

133

much of passing judgment as of evaluating the data to see whether churches are consistent with their purported aims.

At the outset, it should be made clear that, no matter what their appraisal, most scientists do not see an end to the churches nor any value in efforts to abolish them:

Davis *I have confidence in the church and feel that there is a need for it.*

Waldman *I don't think the church will die. It has survived this long. All the different denominations have met their problems over the years.*

Pihl *I have no interest in fighting against the churches. People should be allowed to be missionaries among us, but they should not be allowed to force us into their beliefs. It would be a terrible, orthodox action to abolish all churches. That would also be a religious orthodoxy that I am opposed to.*

This is not the same thing as saying, however, that the activities of the churches are, either generally or specifically, satisfactory to scientists, or that the religious needs of people are being adequately met by the multitude of religious bodies in existence today.

What can science say specifically to the churches? The question presupposes that communication between the two is possible and desirable. Some do not see it this way:

Westphal *Science has nothing to say to religion, exactly as little as religion has to say to science. They have different methods.*

Pihl *I have no message to the church. In my opinion, people should have the right to cultivate their religious interests in anyone they wish to. Science has nothing of interest to the church. My respect for religious people is so high that they should not be influenced by the statements of science.*

I have no idea what the church should do. This is   **Born**
their affair. I am not interested that much in the
organization of a church.

The Human Failings

But there are many who are willing to pinpoint specific failings, nearly all of them arising from the humanness of the churches. If these are faults they are universal, and churchmen can hardly be singled out for blame without condemning the whole human race in the process, including the scientists who are making the observations.

The institutional church is administered by men,   **Ehrenberger**
and everything that is made and administered by
men is subject to error, no matter how highly placed
the men are.

I attend church every Sunday, but I do not have   **Davis**
too much confidence in the people who represent
the church. These people are nothing but human
beings. They have all the frailties and weaknesses of
human beings. We like to think of our leaders in the
church as being up on a pedestal, but this I will not
accept.

What are some of the "faults" of being human? Man, the social animal, seems obsessed with the benefits of organization, sometimes for its own sake. Long after the goals of common activity have been reached, many churches become mired down in the agonizing and often fruitless pursuit of refining, systematizing, and parliamentarizing their procedures, often to the amazement and even the disservice of their members. This hierarchical method truly becomes the message, and the whole system resembles political infighting more than it does a religious force. Endless splintering and warring between the resultant factions is a natural corollary of this situation. Commonness of purpose is lost in a welter of differences in polity.

Davis   *I attempt to divorce myself from the politics of the church and of any liturgy or practice that is a carryover of this political system. There is still a tendency for churches to maintain their autonomy, not so much by the strong support of people based entirely on religion, but through politics.*

Friedrich   *Many churches today are full of little kingdom-builders who don't want to lose their power and authority over their group. They're afraid that if they get too friendly with another group they wouldn't survive. Perhaps this motivates the dividing lines that separate the various denominations. The denominations within the church need to think more about their similarities and less about their differences and worry a little less about purity of doctrine, as they so righteously call it. They need to think more about society and about their obligations to society and what they can do together as a force for Christ instead of how they're different and of being proud of the difference.*

Rydberg   *We should teach religion, absolutely, and they may emphasize Christianity, because it has played an important role in our history, but they should learn much more about other religions. We should, for example, learn that the Moslems, the Jewish people, the Lutherans, the Catholics, all of us have the same basic religion.*

Wolf-Heidegger   *If the church cannot agree on minor points, how can it make progress on the other issues? Its approach is much too academic. Instead of cooperating and working with each other, there is a nonsensical antagonism. This has contributed to my antichurch (not antireligious) view. There should be absolute cooperation between men, between nations, between political views, etc., and absolute freedom to let the other person think and do as he wishes. This*

*must be mutual, of course. That would be a paradise
on earth.*

*The church has to abandon its leaning toward the
establishment. It is defending things other than religion. It is not independent enough.*   **Van Iersel**

The official bulwark of separatism is dogmatism. As a
church body ages, nothing proliferates more assiduously
than its codified teachings—its dogmas. Again an entirely
human trait, dogmatism is nonetheless the single attribute
that violates most directly the method of science. Understandably, then, it is the dogmatism of the churches, the
unwillingness to leave questions open, that antagonizes
scientists most. Their condemnation of it is often incisive.

*Churches might well learn from science to be less
dogmatic. This might help to bridge the gap.*   **Anderson**

*The fact that the church is too dogmatic prevents
it from being specific about problems. The church
cloaks itself in dogmatic statements as a shield a-
gainst society. If it's asked a probing question and
it's afraid to give an answer for fear it might somehow crumble some underlying teaching, it throws
out one of those dogmatic statements like a shield,
but this doesn't answer the question.*   **Friedrich**

*The church has been too dogmatic. Interpreta-
tions depend on time and place.*   **Van Iersel**

*The church can learn something from the attitude
of some scientists. Scientists, more than other
people, should be aware of the dangers of closing off
the world. There is a tendency among scientists to
finish science. For this reason Christianity is necessary for me, to be able to face the questions and not
answer them. If theology could learn this, it would
be terribly good. They are too eager to answer*   **Gjøtterud**

137

questions too. People need help to face the open universe, the open questions.

Autrum *Religion cannot declare something in science to be true or false.*

Hansen *I don't see that the church is succeeding in its task very well. Far too much emphasis still is placed on dogmas and concepts of religious beliefs which I feel no longer appeal to persons of our day and time.*

"Oxford" *There is a decline in belief in dogma, but people are just as interested in spiritual matters as they were formerly.*

Brooks *The dogmatism of the church antagonizes scientists. But it depends upon the kind of dogmatism.*

Forssmann *Science must present its claim to theology and insist that it deal honestly with the results of science and not pass judgment over them.*

Dogmatism is the blood brother of arrogance. It is a human tendency to bolster weak arguments with loud shouting. Ironically, the organizations dedicated to the furtherance of love between man and his fellow often come on strong as holier-than-thou groups with the supposed divine right to preach inspired truths to a decadent humanity.

Beset by uncertainties and reversals in his own field, the scientist is himself engaged in a battle against arrogance, and he feels that the churches can learn a lesson in humility from his own struggle.

Winand *The message of science to religion is one of humility.*

Inglis *The church has a megalomania, both about here and about the hereafter. The church can learn humility from science. It could learn that there is a*

138

common good beyond the church, a gradualist approach to the problems of the world.

Both science and theology must learn and continue to be humble. **Hynek**

The main message of science to religion is one of humility. Dogmatic teaching is the worst thing, the conviction that they have discovered the truth and that the others ignore it. If science can do something, it is to show that we only know relative truth. They must recognize that we only reach partial views and that we have to be very careful before expressing dogmas. Theologians ought to be more conscious about certain principles which derive from science and which they have to use before expressing their views and which they have to mix with the less precise vision of the world given to us by tradition and by our instincts. **Duchesne**

The church can learn humility from the old science, not from present scientists. They have lost their humility. **Born**

The scientist becomes humble when he sees what lies before him and behind him. So does the church. This is the only point where both, as thinking individuals, are very close. Both are humble. Only he is not humble who has no insight. Whoever thinks and feels must be humble, whether it is in science or religion or whatever it is. **Wolf-Heidegger**

The Nature of the Task

In spite of failings, the churches are playing a role in the lives and views of men that may well be indispensable, even when viewed from a nonreligious context. Scientists emphasize the necessity of this role as a "basic training" for a large segment of society, a training that does not end with childhood. They also warn that the role should not be prostituted by artificial and sensational gimmicks.

Anderson   *If one adopts the position that one should work out his own religion, then there is an awful lot that churches do, especially for people who don't think very hard about it and require some sort of minimal education, and for the childhood beginnings of education. They provide the basic training, the content of the social adjustment to other people.*

Worcester   *There are attempts to reach people which may degenerate into attempts to shock people. I deplore some of the rather extreme departures from the Biblical teachings. What is really needed is for people to be given a background in religion which enables them to lead their lives in such a way that they respond in a social sense. The obligation of the church is to educate people in an important aspect of their lives, to fill in a background which enables them to go out, not as a church doing good, but as individuals who lead their lives in such a way that they accomplish what has been taught to them.*

Hansen   *The church still can play an important role in giving a person a reference point and providing him with a source of renewed strength through the services and contact with fellow members. There must be some structure for preserving the teachings and inculcating in people the sense of commitment. That is best done institutionally. But I don't see it happening. I don't see it hitting the kids. The church can make an impact by stressing the concept that God is love, that he that dwells in love dwells in God and God in him.*

Once I went to one of the campus ministry groups, where we were asked by the minister to evaluate the program for their youth. He told us that the week before they reviewed one of these new mod films from a downtown fine arts theatre. They also sent a letter to some activist groups supporting a cause they happened to have, and on and on. I asked him whether he happened to touch on the classical Christian concepts, and he said they have a tough job selling that. They've had their fill of church and Sunday School and all of that. I said, "Reverend, I think you're doing a beautiful job of selling Christianity down the river."

Religious instruction should really be started in the adult years and should be left to the free will of the individual. The reason for so much misunderstanding over religious questions is that many who discuss religion do not have an adequate knowledge of the subject. They have only a partial knowledge of what they learned in their youth, and they have remained on this level of thinking. A child must learn religion as fables. But this is not really religion. It is a childish representation. Religion should be built into the curriculum on the university level. It should be part of a student's general education. **Ehrenberger**

There are those who, like myself, through their religious upbringing and through their personal experience feel that there certainly is a God. If I had had no exposure to religion, if I had gone through my training without being exposed as a child to religion, it's difficult to say what my attitude would be now. **Friedrich**

There is a place for the organized church, because there are certain functions which have to be performed. A main role of the church is educational. It's inconceivable that you can do the big job of educating a mass of people without organization. The other big function of the church is a social organization, and that too requires a certain amount of organization. **Anderson**

Effective training requires an awareness of the changing human scene and of techniques of communication that can effectively reach those involved in it. On no other topic

141

were the scientists more vocal than on the need for the churches to be more relevant in their preachments. Professionally not given to overstatement, these men bordered on the evangelistic when they described the vast opportunity of the organized church bodies if they would but identify and directly concern themselves with the needs of a population that must live with parameters far different from those that prevailed when most churches first codified their teachings. The need for relevance applies to the liturgy, the sermons, the precepts, the socializing, and the whole spectrum of a church's life.

"Oxford" *I went to a service in a cathedral. There were half a dozen people there, aside from the clergy. It seemed to me perfectly clear why. Although it is no doubt a splendid example of a certain type of architecture, it is a dismal, gloomy, unattractive building. The service was unattractive. It was musically perfect, but it was completely uninspiring. People are attracted to churches where the minister is an inspiring person. But, on the whole, church people are not inspiring.*

Turner *The prayers and liturgy become boring if they are not meaningful (as they are not to most scientists), and the sermon has its confusing aspects. The average sermon is taken from the writings of an apostle produced nearly two thousand years ago to a vastly different culture, and the good reverend endeavors to make it meaningful to the present-day situation. It makes about as much sense to the scientist as using Aristotle as a basis for modern biochemistry. Aristotle was a great guy who launched a number of branches of science, but he did make a great many mistakes because he had to interpret his observations in the vacuum of knowledge of the times.*

Rydberg *The church has not been able to follow the development which has taken place. A scientific revolu-*

tion took place in the sixteenth, seventeenth, and eighteenth centuries. Most of what we see, what we do, and how we live today is based on this. The church is perhaps not aware of this. The church has actually tried to fight against these developments.

My children wanted to go to church on Christmas Day. I went there because it's beautiful, with the lights and the music and singing. I sat down, listening with half an ear. I'd heard it so many times as a small child. I knew most of the words by heart. Suddenly it struck me that here we have in our country, at this time, on Christmas morning, in six hundred churches, six hundred ministers saying exactly the same thing. And so they did last year, and the year before, and have done so for hundreds of years. This is not development. It is stagnation, even if the story is beautiful. You don't have to tell it to generation after generation and teach it, in addition, in school. This is not progressive.

Religions change with time. If they are too resistant to change, they may be abandoned.   **Beadle**

You can't isolate people from scientific development. People are too much involved in the whole system, in the development of knowledge in the natural sciences. We must ask the churches to modernize their system, to look for other possibilities to take care of the questions which human beings ask. Natural science does not have the intention of telling people that they should not ask questions anymore. It is only the type of question which is different from former times, not the fact that they have questions. You can't answer the questions of people today with answers to questions asked a hundred years ago.   **Wallenfels**

One should have an organization that gives answers to questions which people ask and the problems of human beings in different situations of their

143

lives. In former times, religion was such an institution. But if the answers are becoming more and more the answers of times long past, if one learns one thing in school and on Sunday a very different explanation is given of the same problem, this is bad for science and bad for the church. It is also bad if we speak of the gap between the answers which are given by churches and the scientific answers which can be given. This gap should be closed. It cannot be closed, of course, by preventing the scientist from doing more research and from asking questions and trying by experiment to answer these questions. Scientists should not be restricted only to technological problems. It is impossible for a man to use the products of independent science and the technology of today and to have the opinion that this has nothing to do with the deeper general questions of humanity. It is not possible to retain people in such a veil of religious context. The only possibility is the rapid evolution of knowledge and the acceptance of natural processes by the churches. They have to evolve outward in their opinions and in the information which they give to people.

Jeuken

The Bible is not a handbook of science. The Bible is a book of revelation, put forth in a language that can be understood by the people for whom it was written. It is the task of theology to make the tongue of revelation clear for our time. When people find a conflict between science and religion, I think it is because of the failure of the theologians to speak the language that is understandable for the people of this time.

Friedrich

Everything that I do more than once in my life I do out of some need. I think this is true of almost everybody. I work because I need to support myself and my family. I participate in entertainment because I feel a need for relaxation and pleasure. Now

144

I might join some organization, but if it doesn't fulfill some need in my life, I'm either going to drop it or become inactive in it. It's got to serve one of my needs. I, in turn, will then contribute to the organization. The church is no different. If the church doesn't fill a need, then it becomes irrelevant and ceases to be a living, functioning group. I think that's what's wrong with the church today. It's not meeting the needs of people. If and when it does, it will begin to live and grow and prosper again.

A lot of pastors will not talk specifically about problems in their sermons. They won't say, "You were hitting the bottle last night and that's why you can't stay awake in church today. Do you know what this is leading to?" They won't talk about the seamy things in life. If we had real interaction in church services, we would have a living church. We need more participation and communication. The church doesn't communicate. It needs to be more unconventional in its services. I'd like to see some-body get up and say "Hallelujah!" in the middle of the sermon when the pastor says something that really means something, instead of sitting there with stone faces. It's like taking medicine on a Sunday morning. You open your mouth and they pour it in and you sit there long enough for it to take effect and then you walk out.

The truths of faith have not changed in the last two or three hundred years. The church should simply translate religious truths into practical living without too much schematics. The parables should be told in a modern language. Christianity must be lived out in everyday life.

Ehrenberger

Sociological thinking today is such that the church must come around from some of its past practices. The church has divorced itself from the needs of the people. It has awakened to this fact and

Davis

*is now attempting to bring about a new situation
and understanding. It's going to be a tough job,
because so many people have lost confidence in the
church because it was operated more like a business
than something which is here to satisfy the needs of
the people.*

*The church has a big job ahead of it, and I see a
great future ahead for the church if it will only step
in. The only thing I'm afraid of in the church is that
it has too many old heads in it. Old people resist
change. We're living in a day of change. All of our
institutions are experiencing the throes of change.
These are not pleasant, but they are necessary. The
churches are beginning to experience this through
the rebellion of some of the younger priests and
ministers and their participation in the various
movements. This is a very healthy sign for the
church. But if the church strangles this, they're in
for dire days. They must accept it and encourage it.
I would only draw the lines at the very, very fundamental teachings of Christ.*

Alyea

*It's so important for the church to modernize in
everything that it does, especially for the young
people, because they will be the Christian leaders of
the future.*

Pihl

*Also in the field of religion, one must be prepared
to analyze even our most fundamental beliefs. I
wouldn't deny that religion is a great force and a
great value for human beings. But all attempts to
postulate religious truths as being valid under all
circumstances and for all times are not right. Everything must be open to skepticism and criticism. Still,
there is a core which you never can define. You can
just see how much religion means to people. You
have to look upon it as a historical and sociological
phenomenon. I am very much opposed to the idea*

*that some part should be claimed, in the form that it
is postulated, to be true in all centuries.*

The church acts very stupidly over against youth. **Forssmann**
*Youth is always capable of inspiration, but they
want to have a basis for inspiration. The church
must realize that the moral precepts of the sixteenth, seventeenth, and eighteenth centuries are no
longer usable today. When you take things that have
been scientifically proved and are quite natural and
label them as sinful and unchaste, then you will
drive youth even farther from the church.*

Science does a lot more than provide the tech- **Alberty**
*nical basis of our society and economy. It is more
than better automobile tires and better soap and
stuff like that. It is, along with religion, a tremendous contributor to the way we look at the world.
Scientific discoveries and theories become a part of
the way we look at the world. It changes our language and way of describing things. If the people in
church don't keep up with this they're in danger of
being left behind.*

People don't like to see phoniness anymore. Peo- **Friedrich**
*ple are becoming more and more educated. The
ignorant people in the past who couldn't read or
write accepted what the church said like slaves or
robots. But people aren't robots anymore. They
think for themselves and they don't like phony
people and phony institutions, and in many cases
the church is phony. It is too unconcerned. It says it
is concerned but it doesn't act concerned. It seems
to want to isolate itself. It's afraid and I don't know
what it's afraid of.*
*Science serves the physical needs of man and the
church must serve the psychological needs of man,
but it hasn't done it. It shows up in our mental
health problems. One in eight people need mental*

help. People don't know where they're going or why. Science can't answer that. It can give people refrigerators or put them on the moon or give them fancy cars or new hearts, but it can't tell them anything about their purpose for being on earth and what their goal in life should be, other than to stumble through life into old age and die. So many of the lyrics of today's songs ask such pitiful questions, such as "Who am I and where am I going?" You have to feel sorry for today's youth. The church should be answering these things, and it's not. It just keeps rattling the same old line. It has to change with the changing times. It doesn't have to change its basic beliefs, but it has to change its way of saying these things and make them meaningful today.

Anderson   *I can't understand how any organization, including the church, can survive if it doesn't adapt to its environment. Science has changed the church's environment, because it made it possible for human beings to control their own processes to a much greater degree. That makes a new environment for the church.*

Trümpy   *The church should either change or ease out of existence. It's a question of the church accepting evolution, the sociological evolution of today's humanity as well as the principle of evolution, which is certainly one of the most significant things for the understanding of the place of mankind. The terrible thing is that the church can't adapt its teaching nowadays to fit the scientists, to bring the scientists back, and at the same time to hold the great lot of people for whom the church is the only hope.*

Hansen   *I feel quite often that the institutionalized church of the past cannot and will not change sufficiently to meet current needs. Nevertheless there are hope-*

ful signs, and the church in our time is undergoing a major revolution. What the final outcome will be remains to be seen. Whatever finally emerges will be far different and more meaningful than anything we have experienced in the past. I would also hope that we would more readily recognize that the great religious faiths have much in common, that each of us in our various beliefs is trying to find answers to some of the most profound experiences of living. The great religious leaders, through their lives and teachings, have set models for us to follow. And what they have said and what they have felt becomes clear only when a human being removes all of the facades that bar his life from contact with others. When these are removed one suddenly has the sense that the powers inherent in the universe are for the first time unleashed through him. One is apt to say, "Why has this happened to me? Why have I been chosen?" At that point a man does reflect the image of God, independently of his particular religious orientation and belief. There is indeed "Good News" if we will only take the time to listen. To my mind it is that simple and also that difficult to achieve.

Reflected in many of these urgent reprimands are the basic religious beliefs of individuals. It is amazing that, as different as these faiths are, the consensus on the possibilities for effective church life in our time is remarkably clear. Far from viewing religious bodies as unfortunate vestiges of an ignorant past, scientists see vital leadership roles for the churches in moral, social, and even political questions if they would but rise to the occasion. Churchmen can and must develop such leadership stature.

The number of those who form their own opinions in religious things and in political things, etc., is much, much smaller than the number of those who live their daily lives by accepting a given political or   **Wolf-Heidegger**

149

religious view. The church has a specific assignment, namely to bring the people closer to moral and ethical principles through examples and explanations, especially those who do not think for themselves, so that they will do the right thing in their private lives. I don't think that this will be accomplished through dogma and liturgy. The church should do what a good teacher and a good father and a good mother can do outside the church.

Alberty *What strikes me the most as we look back over the last ten years is how little a role of leadership the church has really played in social questions. A lot of ferment that's going on is not really arising with the church.*

Friedrich *The church doesn't speak out enough today. It has pulled back into its shell and has not helped people to solve their problems. It is not a living, moving force in today's society. For this reason, the church is losing prestige.*

Brooks *The primary concern of the church should be with communicating values, with providing a forum for discussion of values, and for achieving some kind of consensus regarding values. That's the social function of the church.*

Forssmann *The church should raise its voice and say clearly what it thinks when moral and ethical issues are involved. Hopefully the church will not take another four hundred years to learn this, as it did in the Galileo matter.*

Komar *A child learns most of his ethical considerations from his parents. When you try to institutionalize the teaching of ethical values, it comes out counterproductive. As a child grows up and becomes more sophisticated, he quickly sees the clash between the reality and the values. That's very damaging, because he feels that the values were taught completely* *cynically. The proper role of a religious leader is really that of a philosopher of ethics, giving an interaction and not a pontification.*

As children are raised in a given milieu, they develop a very definite superego. Depending upon which milieu and which society they're raised in, they develop somewhat differently with regard to the group they identify with and what they regard as proper or improper, good or evil. The role of religion is to sort of mold these values in the society. It's a very important and proper role. It's a role that has to be done and that cannot and should not be done by science or scientists, because the values of science are orthogonal to ethical considerations. The values of science are the values of a computer, and you would not expect a computer to make judgments on questions of good and evil, but just on the logical output for a given input.

It's critical for the ethically concerned religious leaders to bring to bear what pressure they have on the political leadership in various countries. The scientist is typically in a rather confused position. How the governments use the power that is placed in their hands by scientists is where the final ethical consideration enters. That's where the religious leaders have a very important role to play, not just to influence the government leaders as individuals, but to influence the whole ethical attitude of the country which is simply reflected by the leadership.

The proper role of religion is ethics, not metaphysics. They make fools of themselves when they deal with metaphysics. Most of the church hierarchy is being shaken up by that, because they sort of downgraded the ethical teachings of religions and upgraded the formalism, the metaphysics, the dogma. That's exactly what's crumbling, and deservedly so. Finally the ethical considerations are coming to the fore.

Worcester   *I am not sure that the appropriate role of the church is really changing so very much. There are a great many things that science can say about man, but it has not yet been able to say very much about the ultimate destiny of man, why he is here, how he ought to deal with other men, the basic moral and ethical aspects of behavior. These things seem to be not very susceptible to a scientific approach. It would be very difficult to show any scientific basis, knowing what we do know at this point, for the belief portrayed in the Bible that, by following the teachings of Christ, one can in fact and without question have glorious life everlasting. On the other hand, I feel so strongly that the teachings of Christ and of the Old Testament can have such an impact on the lives of people, can make such a difference in the way they interact with other people and the way they contribute to the life of the community, that the church has and will have for a long time the same old role of teaching this side of a man's character and his ultimate social responsibility, not only to his fellowman but to his God. I don't think this role changes. It has been misinterpreted.*

Inglis   *Religion gives rise to some social drives. There are various types of do-gooders who have various kinds of motivations. The priest who goes out in his parish tries to minister to both spiritual and material needs. He has a religious drive for some social action. Some of the best social action we have comes from this kind of drive. He feels he is carrying out the will of God or the Christian ethic. We get a drive toward socially oriented activities from an analogous but different type of mandate. We're in a position where we appreciate how some of these wonders of the universe affect the lives of men and we have to do something about it and not just sit in our ivory towers and push our slide rules. We should get out*

*there and help get society organized in a way so that
it can survive our handiwork.*

Science cannot be good or bad, but the scientist   **Autrum**
*can. This is true of all knowledge. I always tell my
students that you can use a knife to cut bread or
someone's throat.*

Can science give any specific direction to theology in its
moral leadership role? Perhaps so.

In morals, you can't deny research in science.   **Horn**
*You have to be oriented in the research of science
and you have to incorporate the research in your
moral thinking and your moral attitude. The basis is
that we acknowledge what we are ourselves, our
needs, and that other people are of the same sort.
When we think of this, we get a sense of reciprocity.*

The future of religion among the people who   **Duchesne**
*think like the scientist is the unitarian view. Then,
instead of having compulsory morals, the morals
would arise from the view of the universe, from its
beauty, which would induce in man the pleasure of
doing well.*

The Pitfalls

If they are to come up to their full leadership potential,
the churches must avoid certain professional hazards. Not
all of these have a direct bearing on the science-religion
question, but they are all matters of concern to scientists
who want to see the churches meet the human needs that
science cannot meet.

The first of the scientists' cautions is subtly related to
an indisputable right and obligation of churches—to engage
actively in mission work. The warning is to refrain from
exaggerated missionary claims, which would again put arrogance in the way of effectiveness.

Forssmann *The missionary claim of the church is a mistaken one. It is questionable whether missions were responsible for the temporal improvement of man. The evolution from Stone Age man to the modern Christian required a long time and I do not believe in the improvements among uncivilized people that are ascribed to missions. They did not understand to whom they were praying. They come because the missionary gives them a new shirt, and so they take the rest with it. In their pockets they still have their old views. Christianity itself required an evolution of several millennia, and it is not entirely a coincidence that the three great religions of salvation (Buddhism, Christianity, and Islam) suddenly appeared in a period of one thousand years, which is a short period in the spiritual evolution of man. In the final analysis, these three plans represent the same stage of evolution in different racial and social contexts. When you plant a potato on sand it will be different from one on clay or on pure humus. So it is with religions too. If the theologians ascribe omnipotence to God, then it would be simple for him to make Christians out of all people. Obviously there is a law connected with this which is not yet knowable or explainable.*

We also have sad examples from missions. My father always said, "First come the missionaries, then the whiskey, the merchants, and the soldiers." In this manner whole civilizations were eradicated who did not want to be converted. I do not find this very Christian.

Hansen *I do not look to the church as an instrument by which, through my participation, I get society's problems solved. My role as a technologist makes more sense to me from that point of view.*

Neither should churches equate religion solely with ethics. The point is a double one: 1) churches must not promulgate the notion that the highest forms of ethics are achievable only within a religious framework, and 2) churches must not assume that their mission has been met as soon as their constituents do, in fact, champion and live out a high ethical code. Failure to observe these pitfalls has frequently brought upon the churches the deserved charge of intellectual conceit.

The ethical point of view of a really decent agnostic can be much higher than that of a Christian, because he knows his life is only one thing and there is no consolation for anything to be done after death which he hasn't done during his life. The sense of responsibility of agnostics can be very high. **Trümpy**

The Sermon on the Mount is the essence of Christianity for our time. I deal with very many people, including many foreigners. I sometimes find that Mohammedan Turks think more like a Christian than a real one does. **Forssmann**

The time has come when we have to work for the cultural needs of people outside churches all over the world. **Horn**

The one thing that surprised me as I grew up was to discover that people who were atheists or agnostics were extremely gentle people with extremely great concerns and cares about other people. As a boy, this was incompatible with the idea of what an agnostic or atheist is. They are supposed to be the bad guys, but actually some of them are very, very nice people, very considerate, worried about other people, sensitive, emotional. It surprised me. There must be another reason for being religious besides being ethical. **Alberty**

The non-churchgoers have always had, as far as I could see, morals and ethics that were at least as good as those of the pillars of the church. It might **Turner**

155

be said that many scientists are like the gypsy in
Quentin Durward. *Durward couldn't understand*
that the gypsy was of no organized faith because all
the world had to be either Catholic or organized
heretic. Similarly, nonbelieving scientists are not
militant atheists, or anything else for that matter.

Hansen   *The difference between humanism and Christian-*
ity, both of which have a concern for the human
being, is very precisely this: Christianity says that
there is something else that drives me, that makes it
fun. There is a real joy in doing this. As a Christian,
it's a happy kind of commitment. I know what I'm
doing because of certain reasons. Externally the two
systems look the same, but there is a deep differ-
ence.

Horn   *As a boy, I liked to listen to adult people speak*
about church. After a while I understood that the
ministers they liked were speaking about ethical
matters—ordinary, natural ethical matters. And
those they didn't like preached eschatological and
real religions.

A third pitfall has directly to do with the scientist's
world. If God has given man the curiosity and even the
mandate to explore his universe as well as the rational
power with which to do it, then why do churches frequently stifle scientific research in the name of religion?
Shades of Galileo! Should not churchmen rather be in the
forefront of the effort to encourage a more complete
revelation of God's handiwork through a variety of ap-
proaches? Stifling a specific effort or viewpoint could
mean the postponement of the very insight or solution
that God wants man to have at that moment.

Anderson   *It's the height of arrogance on the part of the*
church to decide that God doesn't want man to do
the things he's able to do, provided they're not

self-destructive. God doesn't even forbid those by making them impossible.

The church will ultimately accept what science has been able to prove, and science has been able to prove a great deal. The church should encourage a search for truth in any field. I don't see where anyone is going to be hurt by it.

Worcester

To a large extent, our present problems are the product of technology, whether it is our affluent life or whatever it is. Therefore, some say we have to bring a halt to technology. But you just can't turn off that kind of switch.

Hansen

In many cases the church has stated that it shall be a primary force in solving the problems currently besetting mankind. There are problems that are far more complex than we're often willing to admit. No one group, acting alone, can meet all of the needs. Technologists, social scientists, philosophers, politicians, theologians: all need to combine in a common cause. The church, far too often, has tried to go it alone and has not found the answers or instituted the necessary changes. This leads to disillusionment and despair. Over and over again the question must be asked, "What is the role of the church in our day and time?"

Both liberal and evangelical tendencies are necessary in the church. The evangelical aspect is familiar and normal to many, many people. The liberal side also has its own following. The harmonious development of Christianity is assured when both tendencies exist.

Lombard

Some scientists even find the churches guilty of crying "Wolf!" where there is no wolf. Perhaps through the irresistible urge to change the past, some in church leadership positions erect scientific windmills to tilt against.

157

THE GOD OF SCIENCE

"Oxford"   *A conventional scientist would never intrude into spiritual matters. So a conflict cannot be initiated very easily by a scientist.*

Turner   *Most of the scientists that I have talked to don't see what the shouting is all about. They see no conflict between science and religion except for the fact that the religious faction seems to be concerned about our existence, which is confusing because we don't worry about theirs. Whatever conflict there is, is largely maintained by the religious faction.*

Anderson   *Scientists are very reluctant to accept simple answers like miracles. In this sense there is a basic antagonism between religion and science. On the other hand, if you look at the consequences of religion in the teaching of how men should conduct themselves, at that level there is no conflict at all. If there is a conflict, it exists more at the church level.*

Waldman   *Science represents a domain here, and theology represents its area here, and the two don't really have to mix. If anybody's going to mix them, it will probably be some theologians who will know nothing about science.*

Finally, scientists find it regrettable that the formal education of churchmen is almost universally deficient in meaningful exposure to modern science. How can churches hope to recognize the problems of a technological society, to say nothing of assuming responsible leadership in their solution, if the theologians who direct the churches do not have a working knowledge of the methods that underlie the technology? The pitfall is an educational one, and therein lies the best hope of its avoidance.

Bjercke   *Recently a leading churchman attended an advertising conference. When he was asked why, he said that his trade was the first one in advertising—church bells, you know. In a very scientific way, he started marketing Christianity. Well, why shouldn't one market Christianity? If you have a good product, then that's the best thing you can do, to bring it out as much as possible. You have a lot of prospective customers in the country, but you must not say, "Look, you people will go to hell if you don't do what I say." You can't sell a product that way. Jesus has a say about who should be in his flock. That's the greatest comfort we have, that we should be judged by Jesus and not by the different active religious people we have in this country.*

I sometimes wonder about the fraction of pastors who believe what they say. I think there is a good deal of evidence that it is not very high. A scientific training would do them a lot of good. But scientists don't have the time for theological training. Liberal arts training is worth the time, but I wouldn't go so far as a theological training. We've had theological exposure in Sunday School. One doesn't grow up without some exposure to theological ideas. Training is different from exposure. It is breaking down of one's resistance to habit. Inglis

Theologians must listen to the way of thinking of science. The trouble is that most theologians are not educated in the scientific way of thinking. Theologians are nearly always speaking in the language of phenomenalism and existentialism. It is a language which is unclear and not definite, whereas scientists are always asking, "How do you define your terms? What is the method you use?" There is a clash between the way of thinking of the theologian and that of scientists, not because of a fault of science but because of the shortcomings of the theologian. Jeuken

It makes me angry when a minister goes out of his area and fools around in areas that he doesn't know anything about. If in the process he makes himself Friedrich

159

look bad to society, he has hurt the church and the cause of Christ.

Alberty   The thing that is conducive to the education of a scientist is quite an openness about discussing things, a sort of an absence of dogma, a sort of willingness to look at things on their merits and be willing to look at things in different ways. This could be inconsistent with certain types of religious training.

Lombard   In theology they lose a lot of time on things that are internal, that are not the bridge between science and religion. The bridge is the certainty that should be developed. On both sides there should be open-mindedness. On the scientific side they are more prepared to go into religion than the theologians are to go into scientific problems. The training of the scientist is more difficult and complete, and it obliges the mind to reason out difficult problems. If among the difficult problems there is a theological one, they like to grasp it. On the other side, the information does not lead to such tendencies. It is all a matter of education. Perhaps, with a new specialization, the church could find a better way to make the bridge.

When I hear our science students talking fine arts, music, politics, and religion, I am struck by how they reason and observe and read the paper and try to understand. I have never seen that on the other side, because the young theologian thinks that it is his duty, in the highest sense of the word, to save people and to apply charity. That doesn't make for a very critical mind. Only secondly does he think of the problems of the theological attitudes of the church.

Hansen   The church needs to define its role. Is it a preserver of heritage and teachings or is it a place to *which people may come for an emotional uplift and rededication of their lives? Is it an institution that is mainly socially oriented toward solving the problems of mankind or just what? If the church does have answers to questions of this kind and defines its role, then I think it is necessary to see how that role is best fulfilled. It may no longer be best fulfilled according to the patterns of the past.*

8

By the Way

Given the freedom of informality, the scientists who contributed their views to this book often ranged into topics that were not, in the opinion of the author, essential to the science-religion question.

One of these topics was the use of contraceptives, particularly the birth-control pill. Several of the scientists introduced this highly charged topic of discussion as a significant example of science-church controversy in our time. Their statements, both pro and con, were invariably energetic and emotional. In the final analysis, however, the delineation of these views would serve more to highlight the differences between church bodies than it would to shed light on the science-religion dialogue. So the topic was deleted.

Geographical and Racial Contrasts

Another unexpected topic proved to be of greater relevance. The purpose in interviewing scientists in various countries and with varying backgrounds of race, color, and creed was to make the sampling as universal and as impartial as possible. It soon became apparent, however, that there is such a thing as a European view on science and religion, as distinguished from an American view, in the minds of many scientists. One European scientist, in fact, consented to an interview only upon the assurance that this Europe-America distinction would be duly noted.

Such contrasts have many facets, perhaps as many as there are scientists who see them.

If you are an industrialist in America, maybe you **Bjercke**
drink heavily, maybe you go out on quite a few binges, girls and things like that, when you are away from home. But even so you may be chairman of the congregational council of your local church. But here in my country this would be quite impossible. It is so impossible that even people who are not registered Christians, you might say, who are not known to be very religiously inclined, are shying away from church work because they have a feeling that they are some kind of sixth-class Christians. This is the fault of those who have monopolized our church.

As far as I know, in America there are quite a lot **Van Iersel**
of Christians who are against their own official church, which in my opinion is on the whole rather conservative.

Hypocrisy is one of the great qualities of Ameri- **Trümpy**
can life, in a very charming way sometimes. It is certain that religious freedom is not complete in the United States because of the bias against atheists. This makes for an enormous amount of hypocrisy. There is a tradition of agnosticism in Europe, espe-cially in western Europe. There would be more interest in your book in the United States than in Europe, because in Europe the problem is so much compartmentalized nationally and religiously that it is more difficult to get a uniform approach.

In Europe, you have to distinguish between alpha **Jeuken**
and beta disciplines. Theologians are alpha men. We are beta men.

163

Wolf-Heidegger *The European is a traditional individualist. The European scientist is strongly so. When Mr. X and I, for example, have formed an opinion over the course of decades of contemplation and perhaps even decades of struggle (as it was in my case), then I am of the opinion that this is the property and characteristic of his innermost soul. In America they work too much with reports, in which opinions are gathered and collective conclusions are interpolated in order to produce and formulate a body of teaching. This I consider wrong. The question arises whether an individual's religious views should be publicized in a report. I am not afraid to stand up for my opinion, but I find the method wrong. It somehow concerns the innermost soul and the individualism of the European, and I do not believe that one always must take a public stand on these things.*

Davis *Much of my religious thinking has been influenced by my racial experiences. I think this is typical of most Negroes. Negroes are supposedly very religious people. This idea is a carryover from the days of slavery. We are living in the twentieth century now. For the most part, my contemporaries think in terms of religion only from their own experiences and not so much as a carryover from what their forebears may have experienced. That is going to be even more true of the younger people who are coming along today.*

The Stature of Teilhard de Chardin

A topic that should not really have been unexpected, especially from European scientists, was the infusion of Pierre Teilhard de Chardin into the discussion of science and religion. Teilhard, the French Jesuit paleontologist who lived from 1881 until 1955, developed a philosophy on the meaning and development of life that is so unique and so inclusive that it is difficult to make meaningful

164

distinctions in it between science and religion. In his most important work, *The Phenomenon of Man*, Teilhard makes it unnecessary even to distinguish between life and death, between living and non-living matter, and thus completely avoids the controversy over the origin of life.

Teilhard was forbidden by his church to publish his philosophical works or even to teach his views. Even the posthumous ecclesiastical response has been far from favorable. This, in the view of many scientists, is regrettable. If Teilhard is another Galileo he will be vindicated in due time, and churchmen will again have been guilty of stifling a scientific giant.

The rejection of Teilhard de Chardin's ideas by the official church is an example of where very progressive and really promising thought has been rejected. Teilhard is the one man who could reconcile scientific facts with religious beliefs to a large extent. His rejection is a very great setback. Teilhard's ideas are the most promising for developing a religion which could be satisfying to most of modern men. It is really the fundamental work of our times. This is the greatest hope for the reconciliation of science and religion that has come up. The rejection of his work was a very heavy blow to Catholic scientists and to believing scientists in general. The church rejected it because there was no place left in his system for original sin, and for good reason, because it's nonsense anyway. **Trümpy**

Teilhard de Chardin has found a kind of explanation which has nothing to do with the existence of God and all the religious beliefs which are accepted, and it doesn't belittle the notion of God at all. To the contrary, it makes him more magnificent and gives a still greater intelligence to the notion we have of God than before. **Lombard**

Concern over the Atom

Another understandable concern of scientists—one that has religious significance and urgency to many of them—is the control of nuclear weapons. Some of those interviewed were directly associated with the development of the first nuclear bomb. Their reactions to these tasks are indicative of the kind of thinking that will be increasingly important in our technological age, for which churchmen will be called on to provide leadership. A mushroom cloud hangs over mankind. If the effort to avoid total nuclear war is unsuccessful, the discussion of science and religion will be necessary. This issue involves scientists, theologians, laymen, and everybody else.

Davis   *I worked on one of the first guided missiles developed in this country in World War II, and I had no qualms about this. There is an element of patriotism associated with this which sort of balances out the moral issues.*

Waldman   *I was in the bomb business. I had somewhat of a guilty conscience. I was actually on the mission that dropped the bomb at Hiroshima. I was on the ship behind the "Enola Gay." We were involved in measuring the effects of this bomb, with the thought in mind that if it failed we would like to know what went wrong. We were at war. I was a civilian. I knew the people who were out there fighting. I wanted to do my part.*

I started out by moving some equipment and setting it up at Los Alamos. We did measurements for a year, and at that point it wasn't clear just how useful these things were in fighting a war. I asked for a transfer out of this particular thing and into something which was more active. I was transferred into a new group called the delivery group. The objective of this group was to be the coordinators between the project and the Air Force. The Air Force eventu-

ally had to deliver a bomb. This was a classified thing. One of the first things we did was to measure up the size of the bomb bays of a B-29. I would fly for hours, ten to twelve hours, way up at thirty thousand feet measuring temperatures in the bomb bay and vibrations in the bomb bay so that we would have some information as to what would happen to this particular bomb which hadn't been built yet.

Finally the bomb was put together and the tests were made. Then our mission changed. Now the question was whether or not the bomb would go when it was dropped. You get wrapped up with all this—thirty-two years old and completely wrapped up with all this. The objective is to get it done. I did feel a lot of pangs of conscience on the way back from Hiroshima, because as we turned and looked down, there was a pall of smog and smoke over the thing. Then, the next day, reconnaissance brought in the pictures and the words of the tremendous damage, and we had the radio reports from Japan actually coming over, and one had a certain feeling of what disaster had been wrought. I must say that it wasn't until that time. But I didn't have guilt pangs to the extent that I couldn't sleep or do anything, any more than a man who is a foot soldier and fires a gun, or a pilot who drops bombs.

Every human being should use his moral power where he can do it in order to prevent the misuse of nuclear power. This is not strictly a moral problem of the churches, it is also a moral problem of all mankind. Mandel

You might say that we should never have invented the atomic bomb and that those of us who did it were at fault morally somehow. I don't think any group in any country could have prevented that from happening somewhere in the world. We scien- Inglis

167

tists need a motivation that might come from an appreciation of social needs outside of science. Various degrees of religious motivation might help somehow to influence politics. This is the direction that our missionary zeal needs to go.

One of the biggest troubles in getting any sensible move in the direction of taming the atom on an international scale is the tremendous lethargy and ignorance of the people on these things. People have a feeling that the Department of Defense is taking care of this problem and we don't need to worry. There are many people who won't read the type of magazine or book that carries serious discussions of these problems.

The church has a spiritually-oriented educational opportunity which is tremendous. If just an occasional sermon were on the subject of the need for a nonproliferation treaty, or why we shouldn't have a missile site in the area, it would help give the Congressman who is otherwise moving in this direction enough backing to do it. I feel very strongly that the church should take a more active part.

Personal Testimonials

Finally, there follows a potpourri of responses which can best be described as personal testimonials to religious beliefs. In publishing them, no effort is made to identify or to promote a particular viewpoint. They are included here for the sake of completeness and fairness; it seems unfair to quote segments of a man's ideas on various topics and then to omit some of his most personal religious convictions.

Lombard   *What makes man for me is not the body but the soul. We could be a flea or a rabbit and have the same discussion we are having now. We have an animal body, but the form of the body is rather secondary. I understand very well why it is on this body that the notion of divinity, of the future, of the big problem arises. It's because we have the shape which is more fit for that. But an insect, for example, with its social trend, could do the same.*

The European world has developed for two thousand years in the ethical sense that came to the world through Jesus. This was something new to antique Europe, for example the Sermon on the Mount. In this sense I am a Christian, even though I avoid every dogma and have not been a member of the church for forty years. In exactly the same sense, I could also be a Buddhist, since the ethic of Buddhism is very good. One can be a Christian, according to the ethic of the Sermon on the Mount, and live according to it. One doesn't have to believe in the divinity of Christ.

I grew up in an Evangelical home. Shortly after my confirmation, I went to my pastor and told him that I had a problem. God knows everything in the past, present, and future. Yet it is demanded of me that I should behave in a specific manner. That doesn't make sense. Nobody has yet explained this riddle to me. I know that many others are stuck on this point.

Westphal

I am a Unitarian, a person who formulates his own concept of a deity. We have a reasonable approach toward bridging the credibility gap between science and religion, toward selecting what is good of formal religion, but only that which doesn't come into conflict with science, and using the forms of religion to provide individual motivations without the mystical parts of most formal religions. I think the formal religions are moving in our direction in a sense, although there is much resistance against it. I think this is healthy and inevitable. We can't ignore modern science.

Inglis

Forssmann   *Christ gave us a moral code that has been binding for us for two thousand years, which has influenced our whole cultural evolution, and which is so strong that it is workable even for those who steer clear of Christianity. Even the Communists have something like it. They have large segments of Christ's moral ethics. Christ is one of the greatest phenomena of history.*

Komar   *I have changed my views over the years rather radically. I used to have the attitude that the universe really had to be completely deterministic. There are the laws of nature and the function of scientists is to find out what these laws are. Having found them out, at least in principle, you can now predict. Knowing the cause, you know the effect. You set up the initial conditions and the laws will tell you how the initial conditions will propagate into the future and what will happen. This is the sort of deterministic attitude most students have very deeply when they first enter.*

I now believe this is completely false. I don't believe there are laws of nature. I don't think there is a determinism. This change came not from philosophical or ethical considerations, but just from trying to understand the directions in which science has been going. It seems to be going in the direction that there really aren't laws of nature, that there really is a certain randomness. I've come to live with this viewpoint to such an extent that I find it rather appealing. After all, if there are laws of nature, could they have been written differently? What if you change the laws? Then I begin to realize that the concept of laws for the universe as a whole is a basically meaningless concept.

Turner   *I wonder why Christ took, because Amenhotep IV in 1370 B.C. preached the same thing that Christ preached, namely brotherly love. Only Amenhotep* *was preaching it to the nobles and wealthy people who didn't have anything to gain by it and everything to lose. Then Christ came along and preached the same thing to the slaves and the downtrodden people who had nothing to lose and everything to gain. There were quite a lot of other guys who presented themselves as being messiahs and were dealt with rather summarily.*

I would describe myself as an agnostic, primarily in the sense that religion is not very important to me. I support a church, but I'm not a member. My wife and some of my family are interested. I support it sort of more as a social system than out of real religious conviction. **Brooks**

The teachings of Christ are very reasonable and logical teachings. For any era, they're absolutely the reasonable thing to do. What's unfortunate is that we don't live by them. **Waldman**

The Bible is better than any psychiatrist's couch. It's all there. You can get everything you need from it. **Friedrich**

It is important for a person who wants to lead a Christian life to read the Bible as much as he possibly can, so that he can gradually get to understand it. Very few people have the light of the Lord fall upon them, as it did upon Saul, to convert them instantaneously. **Alyea**

The purpose of religion is to show man how to live and to help him. The Bible is its constitution. **Piccard**

I can remember that when my grandfather died, whom I loved very much, I felt a sort of uneasiness and I was glad when the minister said something which meant that my grandfather was in heaven. But with what right could this man say this? And, **Horn**

171

more important, why should I feel glad that this man could make such a declaration? The conclusion for me was that it was humbug. Then, when I studied science, I became very much interested in those matters which had an ethical and philosophical implication. I made the determination that I would sacrifice research work for myself and try to make something for people in our country who don't believe in religious dogma. So I studied my scientific subjects from a philosophical point of view. At the same time I started reading philosophy, but I didn't find one that was the same as mine.

Lombard   *People who try to eliminate the parables of the Bible make a great mistake, because a parable is the only way to give examples across all the tendencies of the centuries. One is a Romantic century, another one is Rococo, another one is a period of scientific explanation for everything. The only transcendent way to transmit a belief is through the parables of the ancients. For example, the parable of the shepherd and the sheep keeps its permanent message in a form which is not very satisfactory for our present mind. We find it childish. Still, the idea is permanent. Christ knew very well what he was doing when he taught in parables.*

Trümpy   *The Bible is a wonderful book. I read it quite a lot, but probably not in the right spirit, not as a revelation but as a very wonderful book. I regard Christ in the same sense, but I hate Paul. He was a very disagreeable person. He was the first to put Christianity wrong. Then in the Council of Nicea we traded our decent Jewish monotheism against this very dubious Trinity, which is just a kind of knee-fall to Roman polytheism and which gave us the possibility to become a state religion of the Roman Empire. This was the original sin of Christianity.*

I have the highest regard for the person of Christ.   **Autrum**
His simplicity and greatness are beyond reproach.
The same is true of his teaching, to the extent that it
is not utopian. Yet it demands too much of man.
Man cannot meet its requirements.

Genesis 1 is an analogy of two times three days in   **Jeuken**
opposition. The first three days are preparation of
scenery: the first day, scenery of light and dark; the
second day, sky and water; the third day, dry land
and plants. The second three days fill in the scenery:
the fourth day, sun, moon, and stars fill the light
and dark; the fifth day, the sky and water are
populated with birds and fish; the sixth day, there
are animals for the land and man who can eat the
plants. The Jews were theocratic, so for all their
doing and not doing they had to have an example in
God himself. They could gather manna only for six
days because God worked six days and rested on the
seventh. So the background for the creation story is
a sociological one. The revelation point of Genesis is
monotheism: there is one God and we are depen-
dent for our being on God.

9

What Now?

Many more questions could have been asked, many more topics explored. But the ones asked and answered on the foregoing pages serve to show how the climate of the science-religion discourse looks to a cross section of scientists of our time. The views are varied, yet often surprisingly unidirectional. The reader may differ with specific items of content or with the arbitrary arrangement of quotations. These are, after all, matters of freedom of expression and of editorial choice. But it is difficult to find fault with the forthrightness and intenseness of the responses.

A final, subjective question remains: Can the reactions of these men be summarized in a way that will give direction to the science-religion dialogue? What, in other words, are the conclusions of the study?

Words, both spoken and printed, are often limited in their capacity to transmit an outlook. No matter how carefully chosen, words cannot totally depict the attitude of the man who uses them, much less re-create the mood that prevailed during a conversation.

Much of what follows in this chapter is based on this unspoken and undefinable aspect of discourse. In a way, the tape recorder has done the job up to this point. Now it is a matter of adding the thoughts that a machine cannot capture and blending these with the recorded messages in order to arrive at some answers.

The Optimism of Faith

Scientists, like all other men, can be divided religiously into three categories: atheists, agnostics, and believers. From the quotations in the foregoing chapters, especially those in Chapter IV, it is fairly easy to recognize the camp of each scientist. What is not so simply detected, however, is the way in which a man views his own religious decision or, perhaps more importantly, what belief or unbelief does to a man's outlook.

That there are differences of outlook cannot be denied. That they are related to belief and unbelief became increasingly apparent as the interviews progressed. Almost by definition, an atheist is lonesome. One man said: "We are, unfortunately, alone here on earth. We have to take care of ourselves." He has no other resources to call upon.

This can amount to a sort of desperation. After the recorder was turned off, the same man confided that if he would come home that night and find his family slain, the only way he could avoid insanity would be to resort to religion! In spite of considerable scientific stature, he seemed a sad man.

More often than not, the avowed atheist also gave the distinct impression that he was defending an unpopular and even untenable stand. He seemed to be debating an unseen foe, although no one was arguing against him. This could not be blamed entirely on the church-oriented atmosphere that prevails to a greater or lesser degree in the countries represented by this study. The atheist simply seems to protest too much.

In striking contrast, the men who projected the most enthusiasm and optimism in the description of their professional activities, as well as of their religious views, were almost invariably strong believers in well-defined tenets of faith. One man literally sang as he worked. Again, no one was pitted against them, but many of these men came on

175

like evangelists for their beliefs, and their convictions are carrying over into their daily work with a consistency that amounts almost to scientific proof.

Lombard

My religious philosophy has given me a very happy way of life. The system works well. It gives me a certain freedom of thinking, of considering things and people. I think of it as a proof by experience, which is very positive.

Churches and Religion

A second conclusion involves both words and mood. As the following statements make abundantly clear, many scientists distinguish sharply between religion and the church. What is especially significant is that the responses were not given in reply to a specific question on this point. Both the spontaneity and the sharpness of the religion-church distinction came as a surprise.

Born

Many scientists are religious, but not by way of church religion. There is a strong difference between the church and religion.

Westphal

Please distinguish between religion and the church. It is still true today that many people retain membership for some very superficial reasons, e.g., baptism of the children, matrimony, and a Christian burial. A man can be a good scientist and be very religious. But I must add something. I understand religion in a very wide sense. To be religious means to be in possession of a spiritual conviction that responds to the needs of men living together, a so-called social concern.

Van Iersel

A man who doesn't go to church can be very religious.

Wolf-Heidegger

I distinguish very strongly between religion and the church. The ethical and moral philosophy that a

*single individual struggles to attain can be con-
sidered a kind of religion, even if it is at odds with
the collective churches of the world.*

*In the course of my life and through various
ecclesiastical understandings, I have fallen completely away from every church. But to the extent
that I have moved away from the church, I have
developed my own world view, one that says that I
am not here for myself but that I have a duty over
against my fellowman and fellow creatures.*

I don't adhere to any well-defined religious faith, **Pihl**
*but I don't know if I'm not to be looked upon as a
religious man. There is a certain type of people for
whom the absoluteness, the orthodoxy, is more fundamental than the content of their belief. You see
such people change from strong Catholic to strong
Communist, and the other way around. They must
have something in which they can believe without
any doubt. What they find may depend on their
surroundings.*

I don't feel that I'm less religious now than I was **Waldman**
*ten or fifteen or twenty years ago, when I was a
good, faithful churchgoer and worked for the
church and helped to count the collection. That's a
period in one's life, and I think everybody has such
a period.*

Many of my colleagues had long and illustrious **Hansen**
*associations with the church. They had been elders
and deacons and participants in all aspects of the
church's life. I now find that many of these people
have left the church because the significance and
meaning that the church once had for them has been
lost. They are now searching for new ways and new
outlets for religious expression. Oftentimes this
takes the form of small group meetings or discussion
groups in which people are accepted on equal terms*

and try to help each other find their way. This was, of course, one of the very early forms of Christian fellowship. And in such groups the beliefs of all are respected. One recognizes that the slick and ready answer is not always there. Each recognizes the other as being on a journey through life, trying in his own way to find the meaning of life and the methods by which one's living can be more effective. There is a need for something beyond that which can only be termed emotional. The one aspect of the formal church service which I believe is missed the most is the beauty of the ritual and the meaning that it carries to the participants. Nevertheless, these emotional experiences can be found in other ways.

I have my own private convictions and outlooks which I continue to live by. Because of these, I am more acutely aware of my own personal role than I was in the past. I have a more profound conviction than ever before of the mystical presence of God and the power of love that is engendered in me. I feel more than ever that man is the channel through which this love flows and it heightens my personal response to this love.

Horn *There is no place today for religion in its classical form. Children should be led, as early as possible, to use their capacity to think, so that they can distinguish between what we can say is certain between us, what is reliable on a natural basis, and what is only a formulation of what people think about reality and which is, in fact, unknown. We should help children not to be afraid about this. We should help each other to preserve the capacity to live happily and enthusiastically on earth, even though we must recognize the limitations of our existence.*

Why these emphatic distinctions? Could it be that many churches have become unwittingly associated with other than religious causes, that a church often appears to the objective observer more like a business or a political action group than anything else? If so, then their value to the individual as well as to society has drastically diminished.

The church should stay out of politics as much as **Davis** *possible. I cannot buy churches becoming extremely wealthy when there is so much need. I cannot buy churches keeping people subjugated. Being a member of the minority race, I know what this means. There has been a certain amount of exploitation of people by churches. It is just against my grain to accept churches controlling people's personal lives and personal thinking. I am a great one for freedom of religion in the total sense—not freedom simply to have religion, but the right to select any religion that you feel you need.*

All churches have spent too much time on the welfare of the church and not sufficient time on the welfare of the people who make up the church and of those whom the church is supposed to be helping.

Religiosity, in general, depends for its support on **Inglis** *the well-being of the carnal world, on economic prosperity. It too easily gives its blessings to the sources of economic prosperity, be they what they may. I'm not thinking just that Jesus placed little value on worldly goods and that sometimes the princes of the church, even these days, seem to be a little profligate in their ways. But it's the rare priest (I know two) who will go out and make a career of favoring disarmament, which displeases the source of much of our economic well-being.*

What the church could do is shake itself loose from its ties to the purse strings of people like munitions makers, just forget that part of its advertising income, and get going on problems of promoting a world without arms. This, to me, is very important, and the church does too little of it. They don't want to offend the wealthier members of their congregations.

Talking about the relationship between science and religion is, therefore, not the same thing as talking about the relationship between scientists and the existing church bodies. It is misleading and unfair to gauge the religious views of scientists largely by their involvement, or lack of involvement, in church activities. This may be a main reason for the widespread view that science is antireligious. Scientists are aware of this view and tend to resent it. Yet they do not have a forum for their stand that has the weight and traditional influence of the pulpit.

Scientists as Resources

Then why not provide the forum? With almost every interview it became more and more obvious that these men were being asked questions that had rarely been asked of them before. Once they were convinced that they were not being exploited for a preconceived and predetermined message, that they were really being objectively probed for viewpoints, their enthusiasm was often surprising. One Nobel laureate, who had specified a twenty-minute time limit in advance, exceeded the scheduled time fourfold. Another one offered to continue the conversation in his home if his office time were not sufficient. A third man let the vice-president of the university wait in an anteroom as the conversation went an hour overtime.

These remarks were typical:

Inglis   *It's good for people like me to take time out to think about these problems. Thanks for calling my attention to it.*

Autrum   *Every analysis, every pertinent discussion among different groups is the only thing that brings us closer together as people. It is a shame when one group, whether it is the philosophers or theologians or scientists, does not find the way to discussion. Only that way can we understand each other, which is the most difficult and yet most important thing in living together.*

I like to discuss religion with my colleagues. I do not feel uncomfortable about it. Maybe some people think it is primitive. I can't help it.   **Van Iersel**

I enjoy talking to scientists about God and about religion.   **Friedrich**

I haven't talked like this in a long time. It's been good fun.   **Hansen**

It seems strange that the achievements of science and technology easily make headlines, while the views of the men who are responsible for these developments are not actively solicited. It has been noted that many scientists are, by nature, reluctant to publicize convictions that are not directly tied into their fields. This reluctance seems to increase with the fame and stature of the man.

My opinion is that of a tiny pebble in an infinite world. I am aware of my insignificance and unimportance. What should my opinion mean for the general public? In my view, not much. It is very optimistic to say that somebody else will think more seriously about these questions when he sees how important my views are to me. It would take a greater miracle than I have seen up to now.   **Wolf-Heidegger**

Nobel laureates are, in certain respects, very unhappy people. Everyone expects them to be very unusual. They must have opinions about the most difficult problems of mankind and must be able to speak out about them. In every aspect of life, they are considered as examples, or at least their opinions are specially regarded. This view is not valid, at least   **Ziegler** *it is not valid for some of them. For me it does not hold true at all.*

I frequently encounter people who have the well-meaning view that the recipient of a Nobel Prize must be counted among the spiritual elite in all areas of human knowledge. In actuality, I am afraid that this is frequently, and certainly for me, an over-estimation.

So we are faced with something of a dilemma. Scientists are deeply concerned about the interplay of their work with the ethical and spiritual values of our time, while at the same time a professional and psychological barrier stands in the way of effective communication of this concern.

There are signs that the impasse is being broken, however, by the efforts of scientists:

Anderson *There has been a very pronounced change in the interests of scientists over the last ten years with respect to humanism and the feeling of responsibility to the community and society as a whole: to the underprivileged, to the question of education, etc. Scientists are no longer as unaware and ingrown as they were ten years ago. We've gone through an age where science has been able to tackle lots of problems and has developed a great deal of self-confidence. At the same time, we can see the possibility of progress in social problems, to which we really think we can make a contribution outside of the field of science, using the tools with which we're equipped. Now there is much more a feeling that you have to participate in the local community if problems are going to be tackled and progress made. The scientist has matured as the whole country has become more aware of the fact that it has some significant problems.*

Much more is needed, however, especially on the part of the nonscientific community, if an effective bridge of communication is to be built. The image of the scientist needs to be changed from a mystical and fearsome figure to one that is human and concerned. A world that can make gods out of athletic heroes and revere their judgments in everything from cereal to salvation can surely learn to listen to the hopes and fears of those who are largely responsible for the wonders (and worries) of modern life. A world cataclysm, rather than a World Series, could be at stake.

Are the churches making noticeable efforts to sound out scientists on these matters of mutual concern? If so, the scientists who contributed to this book are not aware of it. There is reason to believe, in fact, that the opposite is true. A distinguished Ivy League chemist, recommended by several colleagues because of his deep concern on the subject, decided at the last moment to refuse an interview for fear of censure by his church body. Oddly enough, he was scheduled to speak in his church on the same topic only a few weeks later, but he left the distinct impression that he would not be able to say what was really in his heart. This kind of relationship with the church is worse than meaningless—it is deceptive and detrimental.

Closing the Gap

If the credibility gap is to close, some rather bold steps seem in order. One of these has to do with what might be called the theological calisthenics of many church bodies. A study of church history shows that an inordinate amount of the time of professional churchmen is devoted to the formulation of theological distinctions and interpretations. Yet it is significant that few of the scientists referred even to the broadest issues of doctrinal interpretation in their discussions of the modern church—and even those were not always taken seriously:

Years ago students at Yale complained about **Turner** *having to study Hebrew. [Yale was founded as a* *theological school.] The president said they had to learn it because when they die and go to heaven, they will hear a chorus of angels singing psalms in Hebrew.*

Doctrinal hairsplitting is considered unimportant by people both in and out of the church. The life and death of the "God is dead" movement is a case in point. Conceived by theologians, perhaps as a public relations gambit, the controversy ran its course almost entirely within ecclesiastical circles. Not one scientist interviewed mentioned it in connection with the existence of God or even as an example of changing religious concepts. Eventually, the whole dispute may take its place alongside the angels-on-the-head-of-a-pin discourse as a classic example of theological water treading and even of total unconcern with the world and its problems.

Perhaps the difficulty is that theologians, by themselves, cannot ask the right questions.

Gjøtterud   *I have a feeling that many people are asking the questions wrong. They think that the problem is to get the totality of existence inside their own heads, systematized and organized and well understood. The problem is to stay in this total, rich reality and existence with my head which can ask the questions. It is a matter of openness and willingness and ability to stay with the questions.*

Closely related to emphasis on doctrine is the perpetuation of traditional forms of organization and worship within the churches. More often than not, religious organizations can be distinguished from each other more easily by outward appellations like styles of music and vestments than by the messages they proclaim.

The great danger in this religion-by-habit syndrome is that members are lulled into thinking that spiritual stature is synonymous with official church membership. There is little need for the individual to think through and act out a conviction if a huge organization and its trained officials do all the thinking for him.

Nothing could violate the scientific method more directly. Indeed, it is this aspect of church organization that is pointed out by some scientists as driving a wedge between the enlightened and the illiterate—with the churches championing illiteracy.

The organization of religion into churches is a **Wallenfels** *dangerous thing, because the churches have to make very accurate propositions for the solution of the problems which men have. With the progress of science, more and more of the solutions of the different religions will become obsolete. So a broader and broader gap is produced between men with information and people without information. In this situation, churches have to take the part of the uninformed because here they will find much more audience for their pre-prepared opinions. You can control the people as long as they don't know better. This is the main danger for the churches.*

The present hierarchical structure of most churches may even be standing in the way of their mission to man. Even worse, in the effort to remain solvent in a time of rising costs and waning memberships, many churches resort to gimmicks that have little or no religious meaning. As in any ailing business, fund-raising preempts all other concerns.

Where, in all this, does the individual find answers for living? For many, the church has become nothing more than a place for a weekly lecture, often ranging into topics on which the speaker is unqualified, without the opportunity for questions or discussion by the audience.

This image of the church is historically ironic. During the Renaissance, the stress on the rights of the individual spawned democracy in church government. Now the scientific revolution and modern technology point to a religion of the individual that can be nurtured by highly effective mass media, unfettered by organizational patterns meant to meet the social needs of a bygone era. Someone has called the sermon the last stronghold of the monologue. If it is, and if in this time of dialogue the sermon is no longer effective, the church ought to be the first to suggest more useful tools for interaction.

In an age of rapid transportation and instant communication, many a scientist sees church bodies as outdated conclaves. Only when the archaic and largely semantic walls between church bodies begin to crumble can individual interaction between faith and environment assume its proper and most effective role.

Davis *Eventually, over many, many years, we will see a breakdown of the walls that have separated various groups and denominations, just as we are gradually seeing a breakdown of the walls between nations. This comes about through communication and transportation. Science has played a very significant part in bringing people together. As you bring people together and they understand one another, obviously these walls which have existed over so many years, these differences, gradually begin to fall apart.*

Komar *The whole trouble with organized religion is that there is no interaction. They don't present their viewpoint for discussion. They say, "This is the word, boys. Take it or leave it. And if you leave it, you're a sinner."*

It is precisely on this point that the Christian community may be able to learn a valuable lesson from its older Jewish neighbor:

Hansen *A Jewish friend told me that one of the things Judaism has learned over the years is not to put your faith in an institution, but in a family, a small group, in which you can react very intimately and draw personally from. The Christians have yet to learn that.*

Religion finally comes down to a personal commitment. Without it, a man's profession of faith is a farce, no matter how imposing the structure in which he worships or how large the denomination in which he claims membership. Cathedrals were once the most grandiose structures of man and the organized church the most powerful force in society. Modern technology has now provided spectacles that far surpass spires, and governments have replaced theocracies. Yet religious faith still stands supreme in its power to transform and direct human life. Unless a church bends its efforts toward this end, it is not really a church at all.

The major role of the church right now is to make people realize that when they pay lip service to all of these nice things, like the Ten Commandments and the Sermon on the Mount, they should also try to live by them in their daily lives. And they don't. **Waldman**

The criterion of a person's religion can be only one thing, and that is his life. A person's theology means nothing unless it reflects in his daily actions. The Christian life is of much more interest to me than is the Christian doctrine. I don't really care whether there was a virgin birth or not. The important thing is that Christ lived and that he had the teaching that he did have. The particular jargon of the church is meaningless to me, just as the jargon of a mathematician would be meaningless to a second- or third-grader. **Hynek**

The basic message of Christianity is that people should love each other, not out of sentimental love but because we belong to the same species. In trying to do that in my life here, it will not end with this life and with the end of the world. But I refuse to fill in what is next, because I don't know. Christ's purpose was to say this and to say that God is not a **Van Iersel**

187

bad God or a God of wrath, but a God of love who can be sought out by human beings. We can end up with both possibilities and we don't know how to decide between the two. Therefore, the New Testament brings the Gospel, the Good News. That belief I have.

Hansen *The church has tried to be all things to all men. I would rather see the church go down glorious in defeat, but at least have kept its concepts and ideals high, instead of discarding them and in the process losing its significance and meaning.*

Friedrich *Just because I can recite the Lord's Prayer doesn't mean that I believe any of it or understand it, for that matter. This is something I learned in talking to people in the laboratory. When I first got there, I used the standard religious procedure. When they asked a question, I would quote the Bible. That doesn't cut any ice. You don't prove anything to anybody that way. The trouble is, after you've done it you feel proud of yourself. But what have you accomplished? Nothing. You've probably even defeated your purpose by making the other person angry.*

Because of Christ, we can love God. I'm convinced that man cannot by his own strength ever hope to attain immortality by pleasing a supreme being. The only answer is Christ. He did it for us. And when you think about it, how can you do anything but love God and your fellowman? If the Christian church would teach this, forget about details, and talk about the love of Christ and salvation through him and what it means to you in your everyday life, then there would be some real life put back in the church. But I don't know if and when that's going to happen.

Komar *I don't see any organized way of opposing science, except by nonsense. It's the nature of things* *that there is bound to be a clash between individual needs and society and the state and the universe. You cannot organize an opposition to science, because it would have to be of the most stupid sort. To oppose science you have to oppose it not in a negative way but in a positive way. You have to bring forward at each occasion the ethical considerations, the individual considerations, the human element. In a sense, you don't fight science, you join it and you point out constantly that hard physical facts aren't the whole story.*

What type of church orientation will best serve the need of modern man for personal commitment to a religious faith? Are congregational activities and parish lines obsolete? Should the role of the professional churchman be radically changed or even completely abolished? Can spiritual needs be more adequately served through mass media and related small group interactions?

Scientists do not venture to answer these questions with finality. But they do say that there is something wrong with much of what churches are doing and proclaiming today. They do say that today's problems cannot be solved with yesterday's answers or yesterday's methods. They also say emphatically that the problems and solutions are important—and that scientists are concerned and wish to be involved.

Index of Contributing Scientists

191